AQA Chemistry Revision Guide

A LEVEL YEAR 2

Ted Lister
Janet Renshaw

OXFORD
UNIVERSITY PRESS

OXFORD
UNIVERSITY PRESS

Great Clarendon Street, Oxford, OX2 6DP, United Kingdom

Oxford University Press is a department of the University of Oxford.
It furthers the University's objective of excellence in research,
scholarship, and education by publishing worldwide. Oxford is a
registered trade mark of Oxford University Press in the UK and in
certain other countries

British Library Cataloguing in Publication Data
Data available

978-0-19-835774-2

10 9 8 7 6 5 4 3 2 1

Printed in Great Britain

Paper used in the production of this book is a natural, recyclable
product made from wood grown in sustainable forests.
The manufacturing process conforms to the environmental regulations
of the country of origin.
Cover: PHIL BOORMAN/SCIENCE PHOTO LIBRARY

Artwork by Q2A Media

A Level course structure

This book has been written to support students studying for AQA A Level Chemistry. It covers the Year 2 sections from the specification. The sections covered are shown in the contents list, which also shows you the page numbers for the main topics within each section.

AS exam

A level exam

Year 1 content

1 Physical chemistry 1

2 Inorganic chemistry 1

3 Organic chemistry 1

Year 2 content

1 Physical chemistry 2

2 Inorganic chemistry 2

3 Organic chemistry 2

A Level exams will cover content from Year 1 and Year 2 and will be at a higher demand.

This book contains many different features. Each feature is designed to foster and stimulate your interest in chemistry, as well as supporting and developing the skills you will need for your examinations.

Worked example

Step-by-step worked solutions.

Summary questions

1 These are short questions at the end of each topic.

2 They test your understanding of the topic and allow you to apply the knowledge and skills you have acquired.

3 The questions are ramped in order of difficulty. Lower-demand questions have a paler background, with the higher-demand questions having a darker background. Try to attempt every question you can, to help you achieve your best in the exams.

Shows you what you need to know for the practical aspects of the exam.

Common misconception

Common student misunderstandings clarified.

➕ Go further

To push you a little further.

Question and model answers

Sample answers to exam-style questions.

Specification references
→ At the beginning of each topic, there are specification references to allow you to monitor your progress.

Key term
Pulls out key terms for quick reference.

Synoptic link
These highlight how the sections relate to each other. Linking different areas of chemistry together becomes increasingly important, and you will need to be able to do this.

Revision tip
Prompts to help you with your revision.

Maths skill
A focus on maths skills.

Chapter 32 Practice questions

Practice questions at the end of each chapter and each section, including questions that cover practical and maths skills.

1 The ¹H NMR spectrum of ethanoic acid, CH₃COOH, is shown below.

a How many different types of hydrogen atom are present in a molecule of ethanoic acid? *(1 mark)*
b Explain why there is no spin–spin splitting of the two peaks. *(1 mark)*

17.1 Enthalpy change
17.2 Born–Haber cycles

Specification reference: 3.1.8

Key term

Enthalpy change: Heat change measured at constant pressure.

Synoptic link

You used Hess's Law in Topic 4.4 to form enthalpy diagrams and enthalpy cycles. You need to know the energy changes for the steps that take place when an ionic compound is formed from its elements.

Synoptic link

You will need to know the energetics, states of matter, ionic bonding, and change of state studied in Chapter 3 Bonding, and Chapter 4 Energetics.

Revision tip

Ionisation enthalpies are *always* positive because energy has to be put in to pull an electron away from the attraction of the positively charged nucleus of the atom.

Common misconception

The second ionisation energy of sodium is *not* the energy change for $Na(g) \rightarrow Na^{2+}(g) + 2e^-$

It is the energy change for $Na^+(g) \rightarrow Na^{2+}(g) + e^-$

Revision tip

The opposite process, when one mole of ionic compound separates into its gaseous ions, is called **the enthalpy of lattice dissociation** but $\Delta H^\ominus$ is always positive for this process.

Enthalpy change
Definitions for enthalpy changes

You will need to know the following definitions.

Standard conditions are 100 kPa and 298 K.

- **The standard molar enthalpy of formation** $\Delta_f H^\ominus$ is the enthalpy change when one mole of a compound is formed from its constituent elements under standard conditions, all reactants and products in their standard states.

  For example: $H_2(g) + \frac{1}{2}O_2(g) \rightarrow H_2O(l)$ $\Delta_f H^\ominus = -286 \text{ kJ mol}^{-1}$

  The standard enthalpy of formation of an element is, by definition, zero.

- **The standard enthalpy of atomisation** $\Delta_{at} H^\ominus$ is the enthalpy change which accompanies the formation of one mole of gaseous atoms from the element in its standard state under standard conditions.

  Examples $Mg(s) \rightarrow Mg(g)$ $\Delta_{at} H^\ominus = +147.7 \text{ kJ mol}^{-1}$

  $\frac{1}{2}Cl_2(g) \rightarrow Cl(g)$ $\Delta_{at} H^\ominus = +121.7 \text{ kJ mol}^{-1}$

  *This is given per mole of chlorine **atoms** and not per mole of chlorine **molecules**.*

- **First ionisation energy** (first IE) $\Delta_i H^\ominus$ is the standard enthalpy change when one mole of gaseous atoms is converted into a mole of gaseous ions each with a single positive charge.

  For example: $Mg(g) \rightarrow Mg^+(g) + e^-$ $\Delta_i H^\ominus = +738 \text{ kJ mol}^{-1}$
  so first IE = $+738 \text{ kJ mol}^{-1}$

- **Second ionisation energy** (second IE) refers to the loss of a mole of electrons from a mole of singly positively charged ions.

  For example: $Mg^+(g) \rightarrow Mg^{2+}(g) + e^-$ $\Delta_i H^\ominus = +1451 \text{ kJ mol}^{-1}$
  or second IE = $+1451 \text{ kJ mol}^{-1}$

- **First electron affinity** $\Delta_{ea} H^\ominus$ is the standard enthalpy change when a mole of gaseous atoms is converted to a mole of gaseous ions each with a single negative charge.

  For example: $O(g) + e^- \rightarrow O^-(g)$ $\Delta_{ea} H^\ominus = -141.1 \text{ kJ mol}^{-1}$
  or first EA = $-141.1 \text{ kJ mol}^{-1}$

  *This is given per mole of single **atoms**, not per mole of oxygen **molecules** O_2.*

- **Second electron affinity** $\Delta_{ea} H^\ominus$ is the standard enthalpy change when a mole of electrons is added to a mole of gaseous ions each with a single negative charge to form ions each with two negative charges.

  For example: $O^-(g) + e^- \rightarrow O^{2-}(g)$ $\Delta_{ea} H^\ominus = +798 \text{ kJ mol}^{-1}$ or second electron affinity = $+798 \text{ kJ mol}^{-1}$

  *This is given per mole of single **atoms**, not per mole of oxygen **molecules** O_2.*

- **Lattice enthalpy of formation** $\Delta_L H^\ominus$ is the standard enthalpy change when one mole of solid ionic compound is formed from its gaseous ions. This is often called the Lattice Energy, LE.

  For example: $Na^+(g) + Cl^-(g) \rightarrow NaCl(s)$ $\Delta_L H^\ominus = -788 \text{ kJ mol}^{-1}$

When a lattice forms, oppositely charged ions attract together and form a solid. Energy is released. The opposite – separating oppositely charged ions - requires energy.

It is important to have an equation to refer to for enthalpy changes.

Born-Haber cycles

You can work out the lattice enthalpy of formation for an ionic compound using a Born–Haber cycle.

Constructing Born–Haber cycles

Figures 1 and 2 show how the lattice enthalpy of formation is found for a) sodium fluoride and b) calcium sulfide.

- Start the first step from zero
- Positive changes are shown going upwards and negative ones downwards

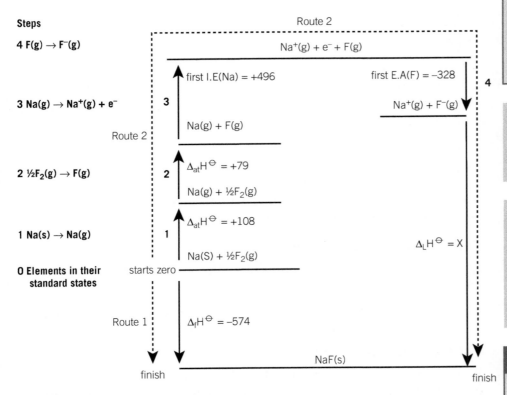

▲ **Figure 1** *Steps in the construction of the Born–Haber cycle to find the lattice enthalpy, X, for sodium fluoride. Enthalpy values are in kJ mol^{-1}. The explanation of each step is given alongside*

The two routes from from $Na(s) + \frac{1}{2}F_2 \rightarrow NaF(s)$ must have the same enthalpy change so:

$-574 = 108 + 79 + 496 - 328 - X$

And $X = 574 + 108 + 79 + 496 - 328 = 929\,kJ\,mol^{-1}$

Synoptic link

Successive ionisation energies help explain the arrangement of electrons in atoms, see Topic 1.3, The arrangement of electrons.

Revision tip

First electron affinities are always negative. Second electron affinities are always positive.

Key term

Born–Haber cycle: Includes all the enthalpy changes for the different steps when an ionic compound is formed from elements in their standard states.

Revision tip

Hess's Law states that enthalpy change will be the same whatever route you take.

Revision tip

Remember that the standard enthalpy of atomisation is the enthalpy change for the formation of one mole of gaseous *atoms*. To form one mole of F(g) you start with $\frac{1}{2}F_2(g)$.

Common misconception

Lattice enthalpy of formation measures the enthalpy change when *gaseous ions* form the solid compound whereas enthalpy of formation measures the enthalpy change when *elements in their standard state* form the compound.

▲ **Figure 2** *Steps in the construction of the Born–Haber cycle to find the lattice enthalpy, Y, for calcium sulfide. Enthalpy values are in kJ mol⁻¹*

Trends in lattice enthalpies

Larger ions mean *smaller* lattice enthalpies – the larger the ions, the greater the distance between the opposite charges of the ions.

For ions of similar radius, the lattice enthalpy increases with size of charge. More energy is released as the ions attract together.

Theoretical compounds

We can predict the lattice energies of compounds theoretically, using the size of the metal ions and the structure of the crystals. Then we can use a Born–Haber cycle to calculate the probable enthalpy of formation.

17.3 More enthalpy changes

Specification reference: 3.1.8

Dissolving ionic compounds

There are three processes *theoretically* involved in order to find $\Delta_{hyd}H^{\ominus}$ when an ionic solid dissolves in water:

1. The ionic lattice breaks to give separate gaseous ions. The enthalpy change of lattice dissociation, $\Delta_L H^{\ominus}$ must be put in.
2. The positive ions are hydrated. The enthalpy change of hydration, $\Delta_{hyd}H^{\ominus}$ is given out.
3. The negative ions are hydrated. The enthalpy change of hydration, $\Delta_{hyd}H^{\ominus}$ is given out.

Question and model answer: To find $\Delta_{sol}H^{\ominus}$ (NaCl)

1. $NaCl(s) \rightarrow Na^+(g) + Cl^-(g)$ $\Delta_L H^{\ominus} = +788\,kJ\,mol^{-1}$

   This is the enthalpy change for lattice dissociation.

2. $Na^+(g) + aq + Cl^-(g) \rightarrow Na^+(aq) + Cl^-(g)$ $\Delta_{hyd}H^{\ominus} = -406\,kJ\,mol^{-1}$

   This is the enthalpy change for the hydration of the sodium ion.

3. $Na^+(aq) + Cl^-(g) + aq \rightarrow Na^+(aq) + Cl^-(aq)$ $\Delta_{hyd}H^{\ominus} = -363\,kJ\,mol^{-1}$

   This is the enthalpy change for the hydration of the chloride ion.

So $\Delta_{hyd}H^{\ominus}$ (NaCl) = $\Delta_L H^{\ominus}$ (NaCl) + $\Delta_{hyd}H^{\ominus}$ (Na$^+$) + $\Delta_{hyd}H^{\ominus}$ (Cl$^-$)

$+788 - 406 - 363 = +19\,kJ\,mol^{-1}$

Lattice enthalpies and bonding

We can predict the lattice energies of compounds theoretically, using the size of the metal ions and the structure of the crystals. For many ionic compounds, the agreement between the theoretically calculated lattice energy and that measured using a Born–Haber cycle is good. But small highly-charged positive ions can distort the electron density around large highly-charged negative ions. This is called **polarisation** and leads to a degree of covalent bonding, see Figure 1. This will cause a difference between the two values.

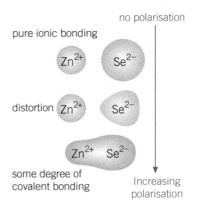

▲ **Figure 1** *Polarisation in zinc selenide*

Summary questions

1. Sodium chloride will dissolve to some extent in methanol, CH_3OH. Suggest which part of the methanol molecule will be attracted to the sodium ions. Explain your answer. *(2 marks)*

2. The lattice energy of potassium bromide is $-679\,kJ\,mol^{-1}$ and the hydration enthalpies of K$^+$ and Br$^-$ are $-351\,kJ\,mol^{-1}$ and $-304\,kJ\,mol^{-1}$ respectively. Calculate the enthalpy of solution of potassium bromide. *(2 marks)*

3. The enthalpy of hydration of the Li$^+$ ion is $-545\,kJ\,mol^{-1}$. Explain why it is much more negative than the value for the sodium ion, Na$^+$. *(1 mark)*

4. Suggest which of the following mainly ionic compounds will have the greatest covalent character: $AlBr_3$, $MgBr_2$, NaBr. Explain your answer. *(2 marks)*

17.4 Why do chemical reactions take place?

Specification reference: 3.1.8

Revision tip

Entropy and enthalpy have numerical values and units.

There are two driving forces that make chemical reactions happen:

- Increase in **entropy**, S, unit $J\,K^{-1}\,mol^{-1}$ – an increase in randomness.
- Decrease in **enthalpy**, H, unit $kJ\,mol^{-1}$ – a decrease in energy.

Gibbs free energy

Feasible reactions are favoured by *positive entropy changes*, $+\Delta S$, (the products are more random than the reactants) and *negative enthalpy changes*, $-\Delta H$. (energy given out).

These two factors are combined by the Gibbs free energy change, ΔG, given by the equation:

$$\Delta G = \Delta H - T\Delta S$$

Key term

Gibbs free energy change:
$\Delta G = \Delta H - T\Delta S$

- Feasible reactions have a negative value for ΔG.
- The entropy change has a bigger effect at higher temperature.
- Under some conditions endothermic reactions can be feasible, because the negative value of $T\Delta S$ outweighs the positive value of ΔH.

So to find ΔG we need to know entropy change and enthalpy change for a reaction.

Calculating entropy change, ΔS

You can substitute entropy values into an equation to work out the entropy change ΔS.

Revision tip

You must divide your final answer for ΔS by 1000 to convert it into $kJ\,K^{-1}\,mol^{-1}$ because ΔH is measured in $kJ\,mol^{-1}$.

> **Worked example: To find ΔS**
>
> For example: $Na(s) + \frac{1}{2}F_2 \rightarrow NaF(s)$
>
> ▼ **Table 1** *Entropies of some substances*
>
> | Substance | State at standard conditions | Entropy $S/\,J\,K^{-1}\,mol^{-1}$ |
> |---|---|---|
> | Na | solid | 51.2 |
> | $\frac{1}{2}F_2$ | gas | 158.6 |
> | NaF | solid | 51.6 |
>
> Entropy of product = $51.6\,J\,K^{-1}\,mol^{-1}$
>
> Entropy of reactants = $51.2 + 158.6 = 209.8\,J\,K^{-1}\,mol^{-1}$
>
> $\Delta S = 51.6 - 209.8 = -158.3\,J\,K^{-1}\,mol^{-1} = -0.1583\,kJ\,K^{-1}\,mol^{-1}$

Is the reaction feasible?

> **Worked example: Finding ΔG**
>
> $\Delta_f H\ NaF(s) = -574\,kJ\,mol^{-1}$
>
> Substitute into $\Delta G = \Delta H - T\Delta S$
>
> $\Delta G = -574 - (298 \times -0.1583) = -574 + 47.173 = -526.8266 = -526.8\,kJ\,mol^{-1}$
>
> So, at room temperature, this reaction is feasible. The reaction is so exothermic that the value of ΔH is much more important than that of ΔS.

When $\Delta G = 0$

When $\Delta G = 0$ the reaction is just feasible. So you can calculate the *temperature* at which the reaction just becomes feasible.

Use the relation $0 = \Delta H - T\Delta S$ so that $T = \Delta H/\Delta S$

Worked example: At what temperature will steam decompose to hydrogen and oxygen?

$H_2O(g) \rightarrow H_2(g) + \frac{1}{2}O_2(g)$ $\Delta H = +242\,kJ\,mol^{-1}$,
$\Delta S = +45\,J\,K^{-1}\,mol^{-1} = +0.045\,J\,K^{-1}\,mol^{-1}$

When $\Delta G = 0$, $T = \Delta H/\Delta S$ so $T = 242/0.045 = 5377\,K$

Above this temperature the reaction is feasible.

Summary questions

1 Using the following values of entropy, S: $NH_3(g)$ $192\,J\,K^{-1}\,mol^{-1}$; $HCl(g)$ $187\,J\,K^{-1}\,mol^{-1}$; $NH_4Cl(s)$ $95\,J\,K^{-1}\,mol^{-1}$
   a Calculate the entropy change, ΔS for the reaction. *(1 mark)*
      $NH_3(g) + HCl(g) \rightarrow NH_4Cl(s)$
   b Explain the sign of the value you have calculated. *(1 mark)*

2 Predict the approximate entropy change for the reaction.
   $CuO(s) + Zn(s) \rightarrow ZnO(s) + Cu(s)$
   Explain your answer.
   Select from: large and positive, large and negative, approximately zero. *(2 marks)*

3 Using the following values of $\Delta_f G$: $NH_3(g)$ $-16.5\,kJ\,mol^{-1}$; $HBr(g)$ $-36.4\,kJ\,mol^{-1}$; $NH_4Br(s)$ $-122.4\,kJ\,mol^{-1}$
   a Calculate ΔG for the reaction
      $NH_3(g) + HBr\,(g) \rightarrow NH_4Br(s)$ *(1 mark)*
   b What does your answer suggest about the feasibility of the reaction at 298 K? *(1 mark)*
   c What does your answer suggest about the *rate* of the reaction at 298 K? *(1 mark)*

4 For the reaction $NO(g) + \frac{1}{2}O_2(g) \rightarrow NO_2(g)$ $\Delta H = -56\,kJ\,mol^{-1}$ and $\Delta S = -70\,J\,K^{-1}\,mol^{-1}$
   a Calculate ΔG for the reaction at 1000 K. *(1 mark)*
   b Is the reaction feasible at this temperature? Explain. *(2 marks)*

5 Use the data above to calculate ΔG for the decomposition of steam at a 1000 K, b 10 000 K. State whether the reaction is feasible at each temperature. *(2 marks each)*

1

first EA(F) = –328

first IE(K) = +419

$K^+(g) + F^-(g)$

K(g) + F(g)

$\Delta_{at}H^{\ominus}(F) = +79$

A

$\Delta_{at}H^{\ominus}(K) = +89$

K(s) + $\frac{1}{2}$ F$_2$(g)

C

$\Delta_f H^{\ominus}(KF) = -567$

KF(s)

All values in kJ mol^{-1}

a Fill in the missing areas, A, B, and C in the Born–Haber cycle for potassium fluoride. (*3 marks*)

b Calculate the lattice energy of potassium fluoride. (*2 marks*)

2 A student measured the entropy change from water to steam using an electric kettle rated at 2.4 kW (2.4 kJ s^{-1}). She let the kettle boil for 100 seconds and found that 100 g of water had boiled away to steam.

At the boiling point, water is equally likely to exist as liquid or gas (there is an equilibrium between liquid and vapour), so ΔG for the change is zero.

a How many joules of heat were supplied by the kettle in 100 s?
(*1 mark*)

b How many moles of water were boiled away? (M_rs O = 16.0, H = 1.0)
(*1 mark*)

c Rearrange the equation $\Delta G = \Delta H - T\Delta S$ to make ΔS the subject.
(*1 mark*)

d What does the equation become when $\Delta G = 0$? (*1 mark*)

e What is the boiling point of water in Kelvin? (*1 mark*)

f Calculate ΔS in J K^{-1} mol^{-1}. (*1 mark*)

g Explain the sign of ΔS. (*1 mark*)

3 Explain why the lattice enthalpy of magnesium oxide ($Mg^{2+}O^{2-}$) is approximately four times that of sodium fluoride (Na^+F^-). (*4 marks*)

4 a Given the following values of entropy, calculate ΔS for the reaction

$MgO(s) + CO_2(g) \rightarrow MgCO_3 (s)$

S / J K^{-1} mol^{-1} MgO(s) 26.9; CO$_2$(g) 213.6; MgCO$_3$(s) 65.7 (*1 mark*)

b Comment on the sign of your answer. (*1 mark*)

18.1 The rate of chemical reactions

Specification reference: 3.1.9

The rate of a chemical reaction is measured by the change in concentration of one of the products or reactants over time. It is measured in $mol\,dm^{-3}\,s^{-1}$.

Reaction rate graphs

Figure 1 is a typical concentration/time graph.

> ### Question and model answer: Finding the reaction rate
>
> The tangent to the graph has been drawn at time = 50 s.
>
> Tangents are drawn so they just touch the curve.
>
> The gradient of a tangent is height/base.
>
>
>
> Rate of reaction at time $50\,s = 0.0035\,mol\,dm^{-3}$ / $120\,s = 2.9 \times 10^{-5}\,mol\,dm^{3}\,s^{-1}$.

▲ **Figure 1** *Graph of concentration (vertically) against time (horizontally)*

Measuring the reaction rate

To measure the rate we need to be able to measure the concentration of a reactant or product without disturbing the reaction. Methods include:

- Sampling and titration. Sample the reaction mixture at intervals with a pipette and titrate one of the reactants or products (eg an acid with an alkali). This method is only suitable for relatively slow reactions as the titration takes some time.
- Using a colorimeter – if one of the reactants or products is coloured. The darker the colour, the greater the concentration.
- Collecting a gaseous product.

Revision tip
The reaction rate at any instant is the slope of a tangent drawn on the concentration/time graph at a particular time.

Revision tip
The concentration of a *product* increases with time, the concentration of a *reactant* decreases with time.

Revision tip
The reaction starts fast and gradually slows down as the reactants are used up.

Synoptic link
The *initial* rate of reaction is measured at the beginning of the reaction when we know exactly what is in the reaction mixture, see Topic 18.3, Determining the rate equation.

> ### Summary questions
>
> 1 Look at the reaction rate graph
>   a Is the species whose concentration is being plotted a reactant or a product – explain?
>   b What name is given to the reaction rate represented by the tangent marked A?
>   c What is the reaction rate represented by the tangent marked B?
>   *(1 mark each)*
>
> 2 Suggest ways of following each of the following reactions.
>   a $CuSO_4(aq) + Zn(s) \rightarrow ZnSO_4(aq) + Cu(s)$ Hint: $ZnSO_4$ is colourless.
>   b ethanol + ethanoic acid $\rightarrow$ ethyl ethanoate + water
>   Hint: the reaction is slow, taking days to go to completion.
>   c $Zn(s) + H_2SO(aq) \rightarrow ZnSO_4(aq) + H_2(g)$ *(1 mark each)*

18.2 The rate expression and order of reaction

Specification reference: 3.1.9

The rate expression

The rate equation, also called the rate expression, describes how the rate of a reaction is affected by the concentration of all the species that may be involved in the reaction – not just the reactants, but other species such as catalysts.

It is of the form Rate $\propto [A]^a[B]^b[C]^c$ or

Rate = $k[A]^a[B]^b[C]^c$

where A, B, and C are species present in the reaction mixture.

k is called the rate constant and is the rate of the reaction when the concentration of all the species involved is 1 mol dm^{-3}. The rate expression can *only* be determined by experiment.

The order of a reaction

The order with respect to a particular species is the power to which the concentration of that species is raised in the rate expression. The overall order is the sum of the orders with respect to all the species in the rate expression.

So if the rate expressions is Rate = $k[X] [Y]^2 [Z]$, the order with respect to X is 1, with respect to Y is 2, and with respect to Z is 1. The overall order is $1 + 2 + 3 = 4$.

Summary questions

1 The reaction
   X(aq) + Y(aq) $\rightarrow$ Z(aq)
   was found to have a rate expression Rate = $k [X]^2 [H^+]$
   a What is:
      i k?
      ii the overall order of the reaction?
      iii the order with respect to X?
      iv the order with respect to Y?
      v the order with respect to H$^+$?   (*1 mark each*)
   b Suggest the function of H$^+$.   (*1 mark*)
   c What are the units of k?   (*1 mark*)

2 a What happens to the rate of a reaction that is first order with respect to X when the concentration of X is **i** doubled, **ii** trebled?
                                                               (*2 marks*)
   b What happens to the rate of a reaction that is second order with respect to X when the concentration of X is **i** doubled, **ii** trebled?
                                                               (*2 marks*)
   c What happens to the rate of a reaction that is zero order with respect to X when the concentration of X is **i** doubled, **ii** trebled?
                                                               (*2 marks*)

18.3 Determining the rate equation

Finding reaction order 🧪

There are two methods for finding the order of a reaction for a particular reactant: a **rate–concentration graph** and the **initial rate method**.

Rate-concentration graphs

Starting with a graph of concentration against time you construct a rate–concentration graph by taking the gradient of the graph at several different concentrations (see Figure 1) and then plot these values against concentration.

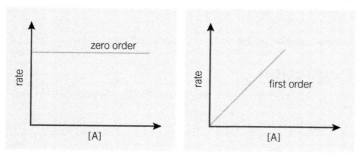

▲ **Figure 2** *Graphs of rate against concentration*

▲ **Figure 1** *Finding the rates of reaction for different values of [A]*

Maths skill: Interpreting graphs

- If the resulting graph is **horizontal straight line** (Figure 2), this means that the concentration of the species being followed does not affect the rate at all – **it is zero order with respect to that species.**
- If the resulting graph is **sloping straight line through the origin** (Figure 2), this means that the rate is directly proportional to the concentration of the species being followed – **it is first order with respect to that species.**
- **Any other shape of graph suggests that the order is greater than 1**

The initial rate method

Worked example: Using the initial rate method 🖩

For the reaction A + B ⟶ products, we do a set of experiments chosen so that pairs of them differ in the concentration of *one* species only. We plot a concentration–time graph for each experiment and draw a tangent to the curve at the start, i.e., t = 0. **This is the initial rate.** The advantage of the initial rate is that we know the concentrations of all the species in the reaction mixture *exactly*. This gives us Table 1.

▼ **Table 1** *Initial rate data*

Experiment No.	[A]	[B]	Initial rate
1	0.5	1.0	2
2	0.5	2.0	8
3	0.5	3.0	18
4	1.0	3.0	36
5	2.0	3.0	72

We now compare the initial rate of pairs of experiments to see how the change of concentration of one species affects the rate. Comparing experiments 3 and 4, [B] is constant and [A] is doubled. The rate doubles, suggesting that the order with respect to A is 1. Comparing experiments 1 and 2, [A] is constant and [B] is doubled. The rate increases by a factor of 4, suggesting that the order with respect to B is 2.

So Rate ∝ [A][B]² You can confirm this by selecting other suitable pairs.

Summary questions

1. Why is measuring the initial rate of a reaction so useful when determining a rate expression?
(1 mark)

2. The following initial rates were found for the reaction X + Y ⟶ Z

[X]	[Y]	Initial rate/ mol dm⁻³ s⁻¹
1	1	1
1	2	4
1	3	9
2	3	18
4	3	36

a What are the orders with respect to X and Y? *(2 marks)*
b What is the rate expression? *(1 mark)*
c What are the units of the rate constant? *(1 mark)*
d Can you be sure that this is the whole rate expression? *(2 marks)*

18.4 The Arrhenius equation

▲ **Figure 1** *Distribution of molecular energies at different temperatures*

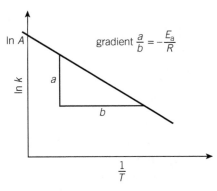

▲ **Figure 2** *An Arrhenius plot*

The effect of temperature on k

Increasing temperature increases the rate of reactions considerably by increasing the number of collisions between reactant molecules and increasing their energy. The latter has by far the greater effect.

To react, molecules must collide with energy greater than the **activation energy, E_a**.

Figure 1 shows the Maxwell–Boltzmann distribution of energies in a gas or liquid. Only the molecules in the shaded area can react.

The shaded area increases rapidly as the temperature increases.

The Arrhenius equation

The Arrhenius equation is derived from the Maxwell–Boltzmann distribution. It is

$$k = {}_Ae^{-Ea/RT}$$

where k is the rate constant, ${}_A$ is a constant related to the number of molecular collisions, E_a is the activation energy, R is the gas constant ($8.3 \, J \, K^{-1} \, mol^{-1}$), and T the temperature in Kelvin.

The equation is most useful in its logarithmic form

$$\ln k = -E_a/RT + \ln_A$$

This means that a graph of $\ln k$ (or the log of anything directly proportional to k) against $1/T$ will have a gradient of $-E_a/R$, Figure 2, so we can calculate the activation energy.

18.5 The rate-determining step

Specification reference: 3.1.9

Reaction mechanisms

Many chemical reactions occur in a series of steps involving short-lived **intermediate** species. This series of steps is called the **reaction mechanism**. The reaction mechanism must be consistent with the experimentally-determined rate equation.

The rate-determining step

In a set of reactions which take place one after another, the overall rate of reaction is governed by the rate of the slowest step which is called the **rate-determining step**. Any species which takes part in the mechanism *after* the rate-determining step *cannot* appear in the rate equation.

> **Key term**
>
> **Reaction mechanism:** The series of simple steps by which a reaction occurs.

> **Revision tip**
>
> Remember the rate expression can *only* be determined by experiment and cannot be worked out from the chemical equation.

Question and model answer: The rate-determining step

The reaction $CO + NO_2 \rightarrow CO_2 + NO$ is believed to take place in the following steps

1 $NO_2 + NO_2 \rightarrow NO + NO_3$ slow – the rate-determining step

2 $NO_3 + CO \rightarrow NO_2 + CO_2$ fast

$NO_2 + NO_2 \rightarrow NO + NO_3 \ NO_3 + CO \rightarrow NO_2 + CO_2$

$NO_2 + \cancel{NO_2} + \cancel{NO_3} + CO \rightarrow NO + \cancel{NO_3} + \cancel{NO_2} + CO_2$

CO appears *after* the slow step so it *cannot* appear in the rate expression. This implies that as soon as some NO_3 is produced it immediately reacts with CO. The actual rate expression has been found by experiment to be **Rate $= k[NO_2]^2$** which is consistent with this mechanism.

> Notice that if you add the two steps together and cancel any species that are on both sides of the arrow you will get the overall equation.

> NO_3 is an intermediate as it is produced in the first reaction and used up in the second.

Summary questions

1 A reaction $A + B \rightarrow C$ takes place in a series of steps
   Step 1 (slow) $A + X \rightarrow W$ Step 2 (fast) $W \rightarrow X$
   Step 3 (fast) $X + B \rightarrow Y$ Step 4 (fast) $Y \rightarrow C$
   a What are the two reactants?   (*1 mark*)
   b What is the product?   (*1 mark*)
   c Which is the rate-determining step?   (*1 mark*)
   d What is the function of X – explain?   (*2 marks*)
   e Which species *cannot* appear in the rate
      expression – explain?   (*2 marks*)

2 The reaction
   $2NO + 2H_2 \rightarrow N_2 + 2H_2O$

   is thought to take place in the following steps:
   $NO + NO \rightarrow N_2O_2$ fast
   $N_2O_2 + H_2 \rightarrow N_2O + H_2O$ slow
   $N_2O + H_2 \rightarrow N_2 + H_2O$ fast
   a Add up the steps to show that you get the overall equation. (*1 mark*)
   b State two intermediates.   (*2 marks*)
   c Is the rate equation Rate $= k[NO]^2[H_2]$ consistent with
      this mechanism?   (*2 marks*)

Chapter 18 Practice questions

1 The following six experiments were carried out to investigate the kinetics of the reaction

$$2H_2(g) + 2NO(g) \rightarrow 2H_2O(g) + N_2(g)$$

Experiment No.	Initial $[NO]$ / 10^{-3} mol dm^{-3}	Initial $[H_2]$ / 10^{-3} mol dm^{-3}	Initial rate / 10^{-3} mol dm^{-3} s^{-1}
1	6	1	3
2	6	2	6
3	6	3	9
4	1	6	0.5
5	2	6	2
6	3	6	4.5

  a What is the order of the reaction with respect to:

    i NO, **ii** H_2, **iii** overall? Explain your reasoning. *(4 marks)*

  b Write the rate expression for the reaction. *(2 marks)*

  c Calculate a value for the rate constant and give its units. *(2 marks)*

  d Calculate the rate of the reaction when $[H_2] = 1 \times 10^{-3}$ mol dm^{-3} and $[NO] = 1 \times 10^{-3}$ mol dm^{-3}. *(2 marks)*

  e Explain why measuring the *initial* rate of a reaction is important. *(1 mark)*

2 The following table gives data about the rate of hydrolysis of a halogenoalkane at different temperatures.

  a What is the order of this reaction? Explain your answer. *(2 marks)*

Rate constant, k / 10^{-4} s^{-1}	Temperature / K
0.106	273
3.19	298
9.86	308
29.20	318

  b Plot a suitable graph to calculate the activation energy for the reaction. *(10 marks)*

  c Is the value you have calculated realistic? Explain your answer. *(2 marks)*

3 The equation for the hydrolysis of bromobutane is

$$C_4H_9Br + OH^- \rightarrow C_4H_9OH + Br^-$$

What is the overall order of reaction?

A zero

B 1

C 2

D Impossible to tell. *(1 mark)*

Homogeneous systems

In a homogeneous system all the species are in the same phase, for example, all gases or all solutions, as opposed to a heterogeneous system where, for example, one reactant is a solid and another is a gas.

Partial pressure

Partial pressure, p, is a way of expressing concentration for gases.

p of gas A = total pressure × mole fraction

where mole faction = no. of moles of gas A / total no. of moles of gas in the mixture.

The equilibrium law for gases

This is just the same as the equilibrium law expressed in terms of concentration (see Topic 6.4, The Equilibrium constant, K_c), but using partial pressures. So for a reversible reaction

$aA(g) + bB(g) \rightleftharpoons yY(g) + zZ(g)$

the equilibrium constant in terms of pressure is

$$K_p = \frac{p^yY(g)_{eqm}\ p^zZ(g)_{eqm}}{p^aA(g)_{eqm}\ p^bB(g)_{eqm}}$$

The effect of temperature and pressure on gaseous equilibrium

Le Chatelier's principle (see Topic 6.2, Changing the conditions of an equilibrium reaction) applies to gases in the same way as to solutions. **If an equilibrium is disturbed, it moves in the direction that tends to reduce the disturbance.** So increasing the total pressure of a gas will move the equilibrium to the side with fewer molecules, thus reducing the pressure.

The value of K_p changes with temperature, so for an exothermic reaction (heat given out), increasing temperature decreases the value of K_p, that is, the equilibrium moves to the left (reactants are favoured).

> **Key term**
>
> **Partial pressure:** The pressure that each gas in a mixture would exert if all the other gases were removed.

> **Revision tip**
>
> Both concentration and partial pressure are measures of the number of molecules of a particular substance in a given volume.

> **Revision tip**
>
> If the equilibrium has the same number of molecules of gas on both sides of the equation, changing the pressure will have no effect.

Summary questions

1 What are the partial pressures of each gas in the following mixture at atmospheric pressure, 100 kPa: 4.4 g CO_2, 6.4 g O_2, 5.6 g N_2? Hint: you will need to work out the number of moles of each gas in the mixture. Use M_rs CO_2 44, O_2 32, N_2 28. *(3 marks)*

2 a Write the expression for K_p for the following gaseous equilibrium. Give the units if all the partial pressures are in Pascals.
$N_2O_4(g) \rightleftharpoons 2NO_2(g)$ *(1 mark)*
b What would be the effect on K_p of increasing the total pressure – explain? *(2 marks)*
c What would be the effect on the position of equilibrium of increasing the total pressure – explain? *(2 marks)*

20.1 Electrode potentials and the electrochemical series

Specification reference: 3.1.11

Measuring electrode potentials allows us to list metals in order of their reactivity as reducing agents.

Half cells

In a half cell an equilibrium is set up, for example:

$$Zn(s) \rightleftharpoons Zn^{2+}(aq) + 2e^-$$

Electrons build up on the zinc and give it a negative electrical potential.

If two half cells are connected, electrons will tend to flow from the more negatively charged (more reactive) metal to the more positive (less reactive) metal, Figure 1.

The hydrogen electrode

Under standard conditions, the potential of a hydrogen electrode is defined as zero. It is used for measuring the half cell potentials of metals. When a hydrogen electrode is connected to another half cell, the emf recorded is the $E^\ominus$ value for that half cell, see Figure 2.

The electrochemical series

This is a list of half cell potentials with the more negative $E^\ominus$ at the top, see Table 1.

When we connect two half cells, electrons move from negative to positive. If we connect a Zn/Zn^{2+} half cell to a Cu/Cu^{2+} half cell electrons flow from zinc to copper.

Representing cells

temperature 298 K

▲ **Figure 1** *Two electrodes connected together with a voltmeter and a salt bridge*

H_2 (100 kPa) →

Pt

$H^+(aq)$ 1 mol dm^{-3}

Cu

$Cu^{2+}(aq)$

▲ **Figure 2** *Measuring $E^\ominus$ for a copper electrode*

▼ **Table 1** *Some values of $E^\ominus$.*

Half reaction	$E^\ominus$/V
$Li^+(aq) + e^- \rightarrow Li(s)$	−3.03
$Ca^{2+}(aq) + 2e^- \rightarrow Ca(s)$	−2.87
$Al^{3+}(aq) + 3e^- \rightarrow Al(s)$	−1.66
$Zn^{2+}(aq) + 2e^- \rightarrow Zn(s)$	−0.76
$Pb^{2+}(aq) + 2e^- \rightarrow Pb(s)$	−0.13
$2H^+(aq) + 2e^- \rightarrow H_2(g)$	0.00
$Cu^{2+}(aq) + 2e^- \rightarrow Cu(s)$	+0.34
$Ag^+(aq) + e^- \rightarrow Ag(s)$	+0.80

▲ **Figure 3** *Figure 3 Calculating the value of the voltage when two electrodes are connected*

1. Figure 3 shows the shorthand diagram for an $Al(s)/Al^{3+}(aq)$ half cell connected to a $Cu(s)/Cu^{2+}(aq)$ half cell. Electric potential goes from negative on the left to positive on the right of the diagram. Electrons will flow from Al to Cu^{2+}.

2. A second shorthand uses the following conventions:
   - A vertical line shows a **phase boundary**, for example, between solid and solution.
   - A double vertical line shows a salt bridge.

- The higher oxidation states are written next to the salt bridge.
- Write the emf with the sign of the right hand electrode.

So the cell in Figure 3 would be written

$Al(s)|Al^{3+}(aq) \parallel Cu^{2+}(aq)|Cu(s)$ $E^{\ominus} = +2.00\,V$

Summary questions

1 a What is the emf if a Zn/Zn^{2+} half cell is connected to a Pb/Pb^{2+} half cell? *(1 mark)*
b Which electrode system would be positive? *(1 mark)*
c Represent the cell on a conventional cell diagram. *(2 marks)*

2 An electrochemical cell can be represented
$Al(s)|Al^{3+}(aq) \parallel Pb^{2+}(aq)|Pb(s)$ $E^{\ominus} = +1.53\,V$
a What is represented by the symbols **i** |, **ii** $\rightleftharpoons$? *(2 marks)*
b State two errors in the following representation of the cell
$Al^{3+}(aq)|Al(s) \parallel Pb(s)|Pb^{2+}(aq)$ $E^{\ominus} = -1.53\,V$ *(2 marks)*

20.2 Predicting the direction of redox reactions

Specification reference: 3.1.11

We can use diagrams like Figure 3 (in Topic 20.1, Electrode potentials and the electrochemical series) to predict the direction of redox reactions.

Which way will redox equilibria go?

Question and model answer: Finding the position of an equilibrium

Will the following equilibrium move to the left or the right?

$$2Al(s) + 3Cu^{2+}(aq) \rightleftharpoons 2Al^{3+}(aq) + 3Cu(s)$$

See Figure 3 in Topic 20.1, Electrode potentials and the electrochemical series. Electrons will flow from Al to Cu^{2+} so the half-reactions would be:

In these diagrams, electrons always flow from the half cell on the left to that on the right, that is from the more reactive to less reactive metal in the electrochemical series.

$$Al(s) \rightarrow Al^{3+}(aq) + 3e^-$$

$$Cu^{2+}(aq) + 2e^- \rightarrow Cu(s)$$

Multiply the top half reaction by 2 and the second one by 3 to balance the electrons, then add the half-reactions to give

$$2Al(s) + 3Cu^{2+}(aq) \rightarrow 2Al^{3+}(aq) + 3Cu(s)$$

So the equilibrium moves to the right, which is what would happen if aluminium and copper ions were mixed in a test tube.

More complex examples

With no metal and two ions such as $Fe^{3+}(aq)/Fe^{2+}(aq)$ we use a platinum electrode to make contact with a solution containing both the ions at a concentration of $1\,mol\,dm^{-3}$ to measure $E^{\ominus}$ as in Figure 1.

▼ **Table 1** $E^{\ominus}$ values for a range of systems. The best reducing agents are found top right and the best oxidising agents bottom left.

Reduction half equation	$E^{\ominus}/V$
$Li^+(aq) + e^- \rightarrow Li(s)$	−3.03
$Ca^{2+}(aq) + 2e^- \rightarrow Ca(s)$	−2.87
$Al^{3+}(aq) + 3e^- \rightarrow Al(s)$	−1.66
$Zn^{2+}(aq) + 2e^- \rightarrow Zn(s)$	−0.76
$Cr^{3+}(aq) + e^- \rightarrow Cr^{2+}(aq)$	−0.41
$Pb^{2+}(aq) + 2e^- \rightarrow Pb(s)$	−0.13
$2H^+(aq) + 2e^- \rightarrow H_2(g)$	0.00
$Cu^{2+}(aq) + e^- \rightarrow Cu+(aq)$	+0.15
$Cu^{2+}(aq) + 2e^- \rightarrow Cu(s)$	+0.34
$I_2(aq) + 2e^- \rightarrow 2I^-(aq)$	+0.54
$Fe^{3+}(aq) + e^- \rightarrow Fe^{2+}(aq)$	+0.77
$Ag^+(aq) + e^- \rightarrow Ag(s)$	+0.79
$Br_2(aq) + 2e^- \rightarrow 2Br^-(aq)$	+1.07
$Cl_2(aq) + 2e^- \rightarrow 2Cl^-(aq)$	+1.36
$MnO_4^- + 8H^+(aq) + 5e^- \rightarrow Mn^{2+}(aq) + 4H_2O(l)$	+1.51
$Ce^{4+}(aq) + e^- \rightarrow Ce^{3+}(aq)$	+1.70

▲ **Figure 1**

The cell diagram would be written as follows

$$Pt|H_2(aq)|2H^+(aq) \parallel Fe^{3+}(aq), Fe^{2+}(aq)|Pt$$
$$E^{\ominus} = +0.77\,V$$

The two ions are separated by a comma and the more oxidised ion is written next to the salt bridge.

Worked example: Will Fe^{3+} oxidise Cl^- to Cl_2?

▲ **Figure 2** *Figure 2 Cell diagram for Fe^{3+}/Fe^{2+} connected to $\frac{1}{2} Cl_2/Cl^-$*

Figure 2 shows that electrons will flow from Fe^{3+}/Fe^{2+} to $\frac{1}{2} Cl_2/Cl^-$, ie the Fe^{3+}/Fe^{2+} system releases electrons and $\frac{1}{2} Cl_2/Cl^-$ accepts them. So the half equations are

$Fe^{2+}(aq) \rightarrow Fe^{3+}(aq) + e^-$

$\frac{1}{2} Cl_2(aq) + e^- \rightarrow Cl^-(aq)$

So the full equation is

$Fe^{2+}(aq) + \frac{1}{2} Cl_2(aq \rightarrow Fe^{3+}(aq) + Cl^-(aq)$

So Fe^{3+} will not oxidise Cl^- to Cl_2: the reverse reaction occurs.

Summary questions

1 Predict whether Fe^{3+} will oxidise Br^- ions to bromine.   *(2 marks)*

2 a Complete the labelling of the diagram below which shows an experiment to find $E^{\ominus}$ for a Cu^{2+}/Cu electrode   *(7 marks)*

b At what temperature should the measurement be made?   *(1 mark)*

20.3 Electrochemical cells

Commercial cells are of three types – non-rechargeable (irreversible), rechargeable, or fuel cells.

Non-rechargeable cells

Worked example: The Daniell cell

The Daniell cell, Figure 1, combines a Zn/Zn²⁺ half cell with a Cu/Cu²⁺ half cell. The copper can form one electrode and the porous pot acts as a salt bridge.

The electrons flow from zinc to copper and the reactions are:

$$Zn(s) \rightarrow Zn^{2+}(aq) + 2e^- \qquad E^\ominus = -0.76\,V$$

$$Cu^{2+}(aq) + 2e^- \rightarrow Cu(s) \qquad E^\ominus = -0.34\,V$$

[The value of $E^\ominus$ is made negative because this is the reverse of the half equation in the electrochemical series.]

Adding the half equations and cancelling the electrons gives the overall reaction.

$$Zn(s) + Cu^{2+}(aq) \rightarrow Zn^{2+}(aq) + Cu(s)\ E^\ominus = 1.10\,V$$ with zinc as the negative electrode.

The Daniell cell is not very practical because it contains liquid.

▲ **Figure 1** *A Daniell cell*

Question and model answer: What are the Leclanché cell reactions?

The Leclanché cell uses a paste of ammonium chloride as the electrolyte. The positive electrode is a carbon rod. The reactions are:

$$Zn(s) \rightarrow Zn^{2+}(aq) + 2e^-$$

$$2NH_4^+(aq) + 2e^- \rightarrow 2NH_3(aq) + H_2(g)$$

We now add the half reactions

$$2NH_4^+(aq) + Zn(s) \rightarrow 2NH_3(aq) + H_2(g) + Zn^{2+}(aq)$$

The emf of the cell is approximately 1.5 V (the conditions are not standard).

▲ **Figure 2** *A Leclanché cell*

The carbon rod is surrounded by manganese dioxide which oxidises the hydrogen gas to water to prevent pressure building up inside the sealed cell.

The **zinc chloride cell** is a variant of the Leclanché cell with a different electrolyte paste, while 'long life' batteries use powdered zinc and an electrolyte of potassium hydroxide.

Rechargeable cells
Lithium ion

The rechargeable lithium ion cell is used in mobile devices. It is light because lithium is the least dense metal.

The positive electrode is made of lithium cobalt oxide, $LiCoO_2$, and the negative electrode is carbon. These are arranged in layers with a sandwich of solid polymer electrolyte in between. On charging, electrons are forced through the external circuit from positive to negative electrode and at the same time lithium ions move through the electrolyte towards the positive electrode to maintain the balance of charge.

The reactions that occur on charging are:

negative electrode: $Li^+ + e^- \rightarrow Li$ $E^\ominus = -3\,V$

positive electrode: $Li^+(CoO_2)^- \rightarrow Li^+ + CoO_2 + e^-$ $E^\ominus = - +1\,V$

On discharging, the processes are reversed so electrons flow from negative to positive. A single cell gives a voltage of between 3.5 V and 4.0 V.

Lead–acid batteries

Car batteries consist of six 2V cells connected in series to give 12 V. The electrolyte is sulfuric acid solution. The electrodes are a lead plate (negative) and a lead plate coated with lead sulfate (positive). The overall reaction that occurs on discharge is

$PbO_2(s) + 4H^+(aq) + 2SO_4^{2-}(aq) + Pb(s) \rightarrow 2PbSO_4(s) + 2H_2O(l)$ emf $\approx 2\,V$

This reaction is reversed as the battery is charged from the vehicle's alternator.

Fuel cells

The **alkaline hydrogen–oxygen fuel cell** has two platinum electrodes in an electrolyte of sodium hydroxide. At the negative electrode, the reaction is:

$2H_2(g) + 4OH^-(aq) \rightarrow 4H_2O(l) + 4e^-$ $E^\ominus = -0.83\,V$

At the positive electrode:

$O_2(g) + 2H_2O(l) + 4e^- \rightarrow 4OH^-(aq)$ $E^\ominus = +0.40\,V$

Adding and cancelling gives:

$O_2(g) + 4H_2(g) \rightarrow 2H_2O(l)$ emf $= 1.23\,V$

This is the same reaction as burning hydrogen in oxygen but the energy is released as electricity rather than heat. The only product from the cell is pure water.

Revision tip

When we add half reactions, we add the $E^\ominus$ values taking account of the signs.

Revision tip

Technically a battery consists of two or more cells connected together.

Summary questions

1 Complete the labelling of the diagram below of an alkaline fuel cell.

(*6 marks*)

2 Fill in the table with the advantages and disadvantages of different cells.

(*7 marks*)

Cell	Advantage	Disadvantage
Daniell	–	
Leclanché		
Lead–acid		
Fuel cell		

3 Explain why hydrogen–oxygen fuel cells are used in manned space craft.

(*2 marks*)

1 a Write the expression for K_p for :

$$2SO_2(g) + O_2(g) \rightleftharpoons 2SO_3(g)$$

And give the units of K_p. *(2 marks)*

b ΔH for this reaction is $-197\,kJ\,mol^{-1}$. State two ways of increasing the yield of SO_3. *(2 marks)*

c What would be the effect of using a catalyst on **i** the reaction rate **ii** the value of K_p? *(2 marks)*

2 a State the units of K_p for the following equilibria:

i $N_2O_4(g) \rightleftharpoons 2NO_2(g)$

ii $N_2(g) + O_2(g) \rightleftharpoons 2NO(g)$

iii $N_2(g) + 3H_2(g) \rightleftharpoons 2NH_3(g)$ *(3 marks)*

b State the units of K_p for the reverse of the reaction in **a iii**. *(1 mark)*

3 $H_2(g) + I_2(g) \rightleftharpoons 2HI(g)$

At equilibrium the partial pressures were:

$H_2(g)$ $2.2 \times 10^4\,Pa$

$I_2(g)$ $0.5 \times 10^4\,Pa$

$HI(g)$ $7.3 \times 10^4\,Pa$

a Calculate the total pressure. *(1 mark)*

b Calculate the value of K_p and give the correct units. *(2 marks)*

4 a Write the conventional cell diagram for a Pb/Pb^{2+} half cell connected to a Cu/Cu^{2+} half cell. Calculate the emf under standard conditions and give the polarity of the copper electrode. Use values of $E^{\ominus}$ from Table 1 Topic 20.2, Predicting the direction of redox reactions. *(4 marks)*

b State the standard conditions for this cell. *(2 marks)*

c Which way will electrons flow if the cell is short circuited? *(1 mark)*

d Write the half reactions that occur if the cell is short circuited. *(2 marks)*

e Write the overall reaction that occurs. *(2 marks)*

f What colour changes would you see if a piece of lead is placed into a solution of copper sulfate? *(2 marks)*

5 Use the $E^{\ominus}$ values for the half equations below to predict whether bromine solution will oxidise Fe^{2+} ions to Fe^{3+}. Write an equation for any reaction that occurs and calculate the value of the emf of the electrochemical cell formed. *(4 marks)*

$Fe^{3+}(aq) + e^- \rightarrow Fe^{2+}(aq)$ $E^{\ominus} = +0.77\,V$

$Br_2(aq) + 2e^- \rightarrow 2Br^-(aq)$ $E^{\ominus} = +1.07\,V$

6 State four conditions which must apply if a hydrogen electrode is to have a potential of zero. *(4 marks)*

Brønsted–Lowry definitions of an acid and a base

These definitions mean that an acid–base reaction need not be in aqueous solution.

For example,

$$HCl(g) + NH_3(g) \rightarrow NH_4^+Cl^-(s)$$

Hydrogen chloride gas has donated a proton to ammonia gas and is therefore an acid.

Ammonia gas has accepted a proton from hydrogen chloride gas and is therefore a base.

Water can act as an acid or a base

For example,

$$HCl(g) + H_2O(l) \rightarrow H_3O^+(aq) + Cl^-(aq)$$

Water is accepting a proton from HCl and is therefore a base in this reaction.

$$NH_3(g) + H_2O(l) \rightarrow OH^-(aq) + NH_4^+(aq)$$

Water is donating a proton to NH_3 and is therefore an acid in this reaction.

The ionic product of water

Water is slightly ionised:

$$H_2O(l) \rightleftharpoons H^+(aq) + OH^-(aq)$$

This equilibrium is set up in water and all aqueous solutions.

You can write an equilibrium expression:

$$K_c = \frac{[H^+(aq)]\,[OH^-(aq)]}{[H_2O(l)]}$$

The concentration of water $[H_2O(l)]$ is constant so we can incorporate it into a new equilibrium constant K_w, where $K_w = K_c \times [H_2O(l)]$.

So, $K_w = [H^+(aq)]\,[OH^-(aq)]$

$$K_w = [H^+(aq)]\,[OH^-(aq)] = 1.0 \times 10^{-14}\,mol^2\,dm^{-6}.$$

Every H_2O that dissociates (splits up) produces one H^+ and one OH^- so, in pure water, at 298 K:

$$[OH^-(aq)] = [H^+(aq)]$$

So, $1.0 \times 10^{-14} = [H^+(aq)]^2$

And $[H^+(aq)] = 1.0 \times 10^{-7}\,mol\,dm^{-3} = [OH^-(aq)]$ at 298 K (25°C)

Summary questions

1 Identify the acid and the base in the following equation
   $$H_2SO_4 + HNO_3 \rightarrow H_2NO_3^+ + HSO_4^-$$
   (2 marks)

2 What species are formed after the following acids have donated a proton?
   a HNO_3; **b** HCl; **c** H_2O; **d** HSO_4^-
   (4 marks)

3 In an aqueous alkaline solution, $[OH^-(aq)] = 10^{-2}\,mol\,dm^{-3}$.
   What is $[H^+(aq)]$?
   (2 marks)

What is pH?

pH is a measure of the hydrogen ion concentration of a solution, $[H^+(aq)]$, using a logarithmic scale.

The acidity of a solution depends on the concentration of hydrogen ions and is measured on the pH scale, where:

$pH = -\log_{10}[H^+(aq)]$

We use the log scale because $[H^+]$ in most aqueous solutions is very small, and the log numbers are much easier to handle.

For example, if $[H^+(aq)] = 1 \times 10^{-14}\,mol\,dm^{-3}$
$$\log_{10}[H^+(aq)] = -14$$
$$pH = +14$$

Measuring pH ⚠

The pH of a solution can be measured using universal indicator paper which usually has a scale from 0 (acid) to 14 (alkali). A pH meter uses an electrode to measure the concentration of H^+ ions directly.

Using the pH scale
Finding the concentration of H⁺(aq) ions

If you know the pH of a solution you can always find $[H^+(aq)]$ ions from the equation:

$$pH = -\log_{10}[H^+(aq)]$$

using the antilog (inverse log) function of your calculator.

Finding the concentration of OH⁻(aq) ions

This takes an extra step.

For example, the pH of a solution is 8.0. What is $[OH^-(aq)]$?

1   Find $[H^+(aq)]$ as above.
$$pH = -\log_{10}[H^+(aq)]$$
so $\log_{10}[H^+(aq)] = -8.0$ and $[H^+(aq)] = 1.0 \times 10^{-8}\,mol\,dm^{-3}$

2   Remember that the ionic product of water is
$K_w = [H^+(aq)][OH^-(aq)] = 1.0 \times 10^{-14}\,mol^2\,dm^{-6}$.
Substitute your value for $[H^+(aq)] = 1.0 \times 10^{-8}$ into this equation:
$$1.0 \times 10^{-8}[OH^-(aq)] = 1.0 \times 10^{-14}\,mol^2\,dm^{-6}$$
so $[OH^-(aq)] = \dfrac{1.0 \times 10^{-14}}{1.0 \times 10^{-8}} = 1.0 \times 10^{-6}\,mol\,dm^{-3}$

Calculating the pH from [H⁺(aq)]

Strong acids dissociate *completely* in dilute aqueous solutions.

For example, $HCl(aq) \rightarrow H^+(aq) + Cl^-(aq)$

If we start with hydrochloric acid of concentration $0.5\,mol\,dm^{-3}$ we know that

$$[H^+(aq)] = 0.5\,mol\,dm^{-3}$$

$$pH = -\log_{10}[H^+(aq)] = -\log_{10}0.5 = +0.30$$

Revision tip

Remember that square brackets, [ ], mean the concentration in $mol\,dm^{-3}$.

Maths skill

For example, what is $[H^+(aq)]$ if the pH of a solution is 4.5?

$4.5 = -\log_{10}[H^+(aq)]$ and
$\log_{10}[H^+(aq)] = -4.5$

Look up the antilog of −4.5. It is 3.1622×10^{-5}

So $[H^+(aq)] = 3.2 \times 10^{-5}\,mol\,dm^{-3}$ to two significant figures.

Revision tip

A solution in which $[H^+(aq)] = [OH^-(aq)]$ is neutral.

Summary questions

1   Calculate the pH of each of the following solutions:
   a $[H^+] = 10^{-3}\,mol\,dm^{-3}$;
   b $[H^+] = 10^{-6}\,mol\,dm^{-3}$;
   c $[OH^-] = 10^{-4}\,mol\,dm^{-3}$;
   d $[H^+] = 5 \times 10^{-6}\,mol\,dm^{-3}$
   (4 marks)

2   Assuming sulfuric acid (H_2SO_4) is fully dissociated in aqueous solution, i.e.,
   $H_2SO_4(aq) \rightarrow 2H^+(aq) + SO_4^{2-}(aq)$,
   what is the pH of a $0.1\,mol\,dm^{-3}$ solution?
   (2 marks)

21.3 Weak acids and bases

Specification reference: 3.1.12

Common misconception

Describing an acid or a base as 'strong or weak' refers to whether an acid or base completely dissociates in water or not. Concentration tells you how much of it is dissolved in water. The two are quite independent.

▼ **Table 1** Values of K_a for some weak acids

Acid	K_a / mol dm^{-3}
chloroethanoic	1.30×10^{-3}
benzoic	6.30×10^{-5}
ethanoic	1.70×10^{-5}
hydrocyanic	4.90×10^{-10}

Revision tip

Always quote values of pH to two decimal places.

Revision tip

The pK_a of a weak acid is $-\log_{10} K_a$

Summary questions

1 For propanoic acid K_a = 1.3×10^{-5} mol dm^{-3}
   a Calculate the pH solutions of the following concentrations:
      i 1 mol dm^{-3}
      ii 0.1 mol dm^{-3}
      ii 0.5 mol dm^{-3} (3 marks)
   b What is the pK_a of propanoic acid? (1 mark)

2 A weak acid HA dissociates in solution
   $HA(aq) \rightarrow H^+(aq) + A^-(aq)$
   What can you say about $[H^+(aq)]$ and $[A^-(aq)]$? (1 mark)
   How do the concentrations of $H^+(aq)$ and $HA(aq)$ compare? (1 mark)

When they are dissolved in water strong acids and bases completely dissociate into ions. Weak acids and bases are only partially ionised in aqueous solution.

Weak acids

Ethanoic acid is the usual example of a weak acid. In a 1 mol dm^{-3} solution the following equilibrium is set up:

	$CH_3COOH(aq)$	$\rightleftharpoons$	$H^+(aq)$	$+$	$CH_3COO^-(aq)$
	ethanoic acid		hydrogen ions		ethanoate ions
Before dissociation:	1000		0		0
At equilibrium:	996		4		4

In this case only 4 in every thousand molecules dissociate. The general equation for the dissociation of a weak acid, HA, is $HA(aq) \rightleftharpoons H^+(aq) + A^-(aq)$

The equilibrium constant for a weak acid is given by:

$$K_a = \frac{[H^+(aq)]_{eqm}[A^-(aq)]_{eqm}}{[HA(aq)]_{eqm}}$$

K_a is called the **acid dissociation constant**. The larger the value of K_a, the stronger the acid, because more of it has dissociated.

Finding the pH of a weak acid

Question and model answer: What is the pH of 1.00 mol dm^{-3} ethanoic acid?

$CH_3COOH(aq) \rightleftharpoons CH_3COO^-(aq) + H^+(aq)$

The concentrations in mol dm^{-3} are:

First write the equation for the reaction and the expression for K_a.

$K_a = \frac{[CH_3COO^-(aq)][H^+(aq)]}{[CH_3COOH(aq)]}$

	$CH_3COOH(aq)$	$\rightarrow$	$CH_3COO^-(aq)$	$+$	$H^+(aq)$
Before dissociation:	1.00		0		0
At equilibrium:	$1.00 - [CH_3COO^-(aq)]$		$[CH_3COO^-(aq)]$		$[H^+(aq)]$

But as each CH_3COOH molecule that dissociates produces one CH_3COO^- ion and one H^+ ion:

$[CH_3COO^-(aq)] = [H^+(aq)]$

$K_a = \frac{[H^+(aq)]^2}{1.00}$

The degree of dissociation of ethanoic acid is very small (it is a weak acid), so $[H^+(aq)]_{eqm}$ is so small that $1.00 - [H^+(aq)] \approx 1.00$

From Table 1, K_a for ethanoic acid = 1.70×10^{-5} mol dm^{-3}

So $1.70 \times 10^{-5} = [H^+(aq)]^2$

$[H^+(aq)] = \sqrt{1.70 \times 10^{-5}}$

and $[H^+(aq)] = 4.12 \times 10^{-3}$ mol dm^{-3}

Taking logs: $\log[H^+(aq)] = -2.385$

so pH = 2.385 = 2.39 to 2 d.p

21.4 Acid–base titrations

🧪 During a titration, the pH of the solution in the flask can be followed with a pH meter, see Figure 1.

pH curves for acid–base titrations

The curves in Figure 2 are obtained by adding a base to a **monoprotic** acid (for example HCl).

> **Revision tip**
> Titrations are introduced in Topic 2.5, Balanced equations and related calculations.

a strong acid and strong base

b strong acid and weak base

c weak acid and weak base

d weak acid and strong base

▲ **Figure 2** *Graphs of pH changes for titrations of different acids and bases*

- Each curve has almost horizontal sections where a lot of base can be added without changing the pH much.

- There is also a very steep portion of each curve, except weak acid–weak base, where a single drop of base changes the pH by several units.

The equivalence point

In a titration, the **equivalence point** is the point at which sufficient base has been added to just react with all the acid (or vice versa). In each of the titrations in Figure 2 the equivalence point is reached after 25.0 cm³ of base has been added. Note that the pH at the equivalence point is not always exactly 7.

▲ **Figure 1** *Apparatus to investigate pH changes using a pH meter*

Summary questions

1 The curves below show the titration of two different acids A and B with sodium hydroxide.

   a Which acid is the strong acid? *(1 mark)*

   b Why are the two curves the same in the region marked C? *(1 mark)*

   c i What is the name of the point when exactly 50 cm³ of sodium hydroxide have been added?

   ii What is the significance of this point? *(2 marks)*

21.5 Choice of indicators for titrations

Specification reference: 3.1.12

▲ **Figure 1**

▲ **Figure 2**

▲ **Figure 3**

▲ **Figure 4**

Choosing an indicator

When you do an acid–base titration, your chosen indicator must tell you when there are the same number of hydrogen ions as hydroxide ions in your flask. This point is called the **equivalence point**. The **end point** of a titration is when one drop of added acid (or base) changes the colour of the indicator. These may not be the same unless you choose the correct indicator for your titration.

Properties of a suitable indicator

The end point and the equivalence point must be the same. The colour change must be sharp at the end point. The colour change must be easy to recognise.

Titration curves

▼ **Table 1** *Some common indicators*

Indicator	pK_a value	Colour change												
methyl orange	3.7		red		change						yellow			
phenolphthalein	9.3				colourless						change		red	
		0	1	2	3	4	5	6	7	8	9	10	11	12	13	14 pH

0 very acidic — 7 neutral — 14 very alkaline

Figures 1–4 are pH curves for titrations of different combinations of weak and strong acids and bases. In each of these cases the indicator must change at the equivalence point when 25 cm³ of base are added to 25 cm³ of acid.

Figure 1 **Strong acid and strong base**. We need the indicator change to lie within the vertical portion of the pH curve. Both these indicators change when exactly 25 cm³ of base has been added so both would work.

Figure 2 **Weak acid and strong base**. Methyl orange changes colour too soon after the base is added, so phenolphthalein is the right choice here.

Figure 3 **Strong acid and weak base**. Phenolphthalein changes colour too late, so methyl orange is the right choice here.

Figure 4 **Weak acid and weak base.** Neither indicator will work.

The half-neutralisation point

On every titration curve there is always a very gently sloping, almost horizontal gradient on the left-hand side. As you add acid (or base), there is very little change to the pH, almost up to the volume of the equivalence point.

- The point halfway between the zero and the equivalence point is the **half-neutralisation point**. So you know you can add acid or base up to here and the pH will hardly change.
- The pH at the half neutralisation point is the pKa of a weak acid.

Summary questions

1 Explain why universal indicator is unsuitable for any titration. (*2 marks*)

2 Bromophenol blue changes colour between pH 4.5 and 5.5. State which of the types of titration above (Figures 1–4) it would be suitable for. (*2 marks*)

21.6 Buffer solutions

Specification reference: 3.1.12

How buffers work

Buffers keep the concentration of hydrogen ions and hydroxide ions in a solution almost unchanged. They create an equilibrium reaction so that either additional hydrogen ions or hydroxide ions are removed if these are added.

Key term

Buffers: Solutions that can resist changes of pH when small amounts of acid or alkali are added to them.

Acidic buffers

An acidic buffer is made from a mixture of a weak acid and a soluble salt of that acid. It will maintain a pH of below 7 (acidic).

A weak acid, HA, dissociates in solution:
$$HA(aq) \rightleftharpoons H^+(aq) + A^-(aq)$$

We add to this enough of a soluble salt containing A^- so that there is a similar concentration of A^- ions and HA.

- If we add H^+ ions, Le Chatelier's principle says that the equilibrium moves to the left, removing the added acid.
- If we add OH^- ions, they will combine with the H^+ ions to form water ($H^+(aq) + OH^-(aq) \rightarrow H_2O(l)$) and the equilibrium will move to the right – more HA will dissociate to restore the H^+ ion concentration.

So both added H^+ and OH^- can be removed.

Buffers don't ensure that *no* change in pH occurs. The addition of acid or alkali will still change the pH, but only slightly. It is possible to saturate a buffer by adding so much acid or alkali that all of the available HA or A^- is used up.

Another way of making a buffer is by neutralising a weak acid with an alkali such as sodium hydroxide. If you neutralise half the acid (see Topic 21.5, Choice of indicators for titrations) you end up with a buffer whose pH is equal to the pK_a of the acid, as the solution contains an equal supply of HA and A^-.

At half-neutralisation: pH = pK_a

Basic buffers

Basic buffers also resist change but maintain a pH at above 7. They are made from a mixture of a weak base and a soluble salt of that base, for example, a mixture of aqueous ammonia and ammonium chloride, $NH_4^+Cl^-$.

In this case:

- The aqueous ammonia removes added H^+:
  $$NH_3(aq) + H^+(aq) \rightarrow NH_4^+(aq)$$
- The ammonium ion, NH_4^+, removes added OH^-:
  $$NH_4^+(aq) + OH^-(aq) \rightarrow NH_3(aq) + H_2O(l)$$

Some examples of buffers

Blood is buffered so that the pH is maintained at approximately 7.4. A change of as little as 0.5 of a pH unit may be fatal. Detergents and shampoos are buffered. If they become too acidic or too alkaline, they could damage fabric or skin and hair. Buffers are important in brewing – the enzymes that control many of the reactions involved work best at specific pH values.

Synoptic link

Le Chatelier's principle is covered in Topic 6.2, Changing the conditions of an equilibrium reaction.

Calculating the pH of a buffer

Buffers can be made which will maintain different pHs.

When a weak acid dissociates:
$$HA(aq) \rightleftharpoons H^+(aq) + A^-(aq)$$

$$K_a = \frac{[H^+(aq)][A^-(aq)]}{[HA(aq)]}$$

You can use this expression to calculate the pH of buffers.

pH of the buffer $= pK_a$ CH$_3$COOH
$= 4.77$

▲ **Figure 1** *Making a buffer*

Question and model answer: Finding the pH of a buffer

A buffer consists of 0.100 mol dm^{-3} ethanoic acid and 0.100 mol dm^{-3} sodium ethanoate [see Figure 1]. What is the pH of the buffer?
[K_a for ethanoic acid is 1.70×10^{-5}, p$K_a = 4.77$.]

Calculate [H$^+$(aq)] from the equation.

$$K_a = \frac{[H^+(aq)][A^-(aq)]}{[HA(aq)]}$$

Sodium ethanoate is fully dissociated, so [A$^-$(aq)] = 0.100 mol dm^{-3}
Ethanoic acid is almost undissociated, so [HA(aq)] ≈ 0.100 mol dm^{-3}

So $\quad 1.70 \times 10^{-5} = [H^+(aq)] \times \dfrac{0.100}{0.100}$

$\qquad 1.70 \times 10^{-5} = [H^+(aq)]$

And $\qquad pH = -\log_{10}[H^+(aq)]$

$\qquad\qquad pH = 4.77$

Notice that when you have equal concentrations of acid and salt, the pH of the buffer is equal to the pK_a of the acid used, and this is exactly the same case as the half-neutralisation point.

Summary questions

1   Explain why sulfuric acid and sodium sulfate could not make an acidic buffer. *(1 mark)*

2   Which of the following mixtures could make a basic buffer? **a** ammonia and ammonium bromide, **b** sulfuric acid and potassium sulfate, **c** ammonia and water, **d** sodium hydroxide and sodium chloride. *(1 mark)*

3   What would be the pH of a buffer which is 0.1 mol dm^{-3} ethanoic acid and 0.05 mol dm^{-3} in sodium ethanoate? The pK_a of ethanoic acid is 4.77. *(1 mark)*

Chapter 21 Practice questions

1 Calculate the pH of the following solutions:

    a hydrochloric acid of concentration $0.5 \, mol \, dm^{-3}$ (*1 mark*)

    b sulfuric acid (a diprotic acid) of concentration $0.1 \, mol \, dm^{-3}$ (*1 mark*)

    c benzoic acid (a weak acid, $K_a = 6.3 \times 10^{-5} \, mol \, dm^{-3}$) of concentration $0.1 \, mol \, dm^{-3}$ (*2 marks*)

    d potassium hydroxide of concentration $0.001 \, mol \, dm^{-3}$ (*2 marks*)

    e a mixture which is $0.10 \, mol \, dm^{-3}$ in propanoic acid ($K_a = 1.35 \times 10^{-5} \, mol \, dm^{-3}$) and $0.05 \, mol \, dm^{-3}$ in sodium propanoate.   (*2 marks*)

2 a Write an equation for the dissociation of propanoic acid, CH_3CH_2COOH.   (*1 mark*)

    b State the expression for the acid dissociation constant, K_a, for propanoic acid.   (*1 mark*)

    c The value of K_a for propanoic acid is $1.35 \times 10^{-5} \, mol \, dm^{-3}$. Calculate the pH of **i** $0.1 \, mol \, dm^{-3}$ solution of propanoic acid. **ii** a buffer solution which is $0.1 \, mol \, dm^{-3}$ in both propanoic acid and sodium propanoate.   (*2 marks each*)

3 The pH of a $0.1 \, mol \, dm^{-3}$ solution of ethanoic acid is 2.88. Calculate:

    a $[H^+(aq)]$ in this solution

    b the value of K_a and pK_a for ethanoic acid.   (*6 marks*)

22.1 Reactions of Period 3 elements

The elements of Period 3 are Na, Mg, Al, Si, P, S, Cl, Ar.

The elements – trends

From left to right across the period you go from metals to non-metals. Silicon, in the middle is a semi-metal and conducts electricity somewhat. Argon is a noble gas.

Redox reactions

All the reactions of the elements are redox reactions because the elements always start with oxidation state zero.

Reactions of the elements

Reaction with water

Sodium reacts vigorously with water, while magnesium reacts slowly with water and vigorously with steam. Make sure you can write balanced equations and work out the oxidation states (shown above the equations).

$$\overset{0}{2Na(s)} + \overset{+1\ -2}{2H_2O(l)} \rightarrow \overset{+1\ -2\ +1}{2NaOH(aq)} + \overset{0}{H_2(g)} \quad \text{pH of resulting solution 13–14}$$

$$\overset{0}{Mg(s)} + \overset{+1\ -2}{2H_2O(l)} \rightarrow \overset{+2\ -2\ +1}{MgOH_2(aq)} + \overset{0}{H_2(g)}$$

the pH of the resulting solution is about 10 – less alkaline because magnesium hydroxide is only sparingly soluble.

Reaction with oxygen

All the elements from sodium to sulfur react directly with oxygen. The metals burn vigorously to form basic oxides while the non-metals form acidic ones. Silicon dioxide is insoluble.

$2Na(s) + \frac{1}{2}O_2(g) \rightarrow Na_2O(s)$ – place hot sodium in a gas jar of oxygen.

$Mg(s) + \frac{1}{2}O_2(g) \rightarrow MgO(s)$ – place burning magnesium ribbon in a gas jar of oxygen.

$4Al(s) + 3O_2(g) \rightarrow 2Al_2O_3(s)$ – sprinkle aluminium powder into a Bunsen flame.

Everyday aluminium items appear unreactive to air or water. Aluminium is coated with a thin but tough layer of oxide which protects it. Once scratched, the aluminium is so reactive that a new layer of oxide forms immediately.

$Si(s) + O_2(g) \rightarrow SiO_2(s)$

$4P(s) + 5O_2(g) \rightarrow P_4O_{10}(s)$ – some P_2O_3 forms if the supply of oxygen is limited.

$S(s) + O_2(g) \rightarrow SO_2(g)$ – some SO_3 may also form

Revision tip

Oxidation states are sometimes called oxidation numbers.

Revision tip

The sum of the oxidation states (taking account of the number of each atom) should be the same on each side of an equation.

Revision tip

Make sure that you can work out the oxidation state of each atom in all these equations.

Revision tip

Phosphorus has two **allotropes** – red and white. White phosphorus will spontaneously ignite in air.

Synoptic link

All the metal oxides are white as the metals have no part-filled d-orbitals – see Topic 23.3, Coloured ions.

Summary questions

1 Write a balanced equation for the reaction of magnesium oxide with steam to form magnesium oxide and hydrogen. Include state symbols and oxidation states. *(4 marks)*

2 Show that the sum of the oxidation states of the elements in phosphorus pentoxide is zero. *(2 marks)*

3 Sodium can form another oxide, sodium peroxide, Na_2O_2. State the oxidation state of each atom. *(2 marks)*

22.2 The oxides of elements in Period 3

Specification reference: 3.2.4

Bonding and structure of the oxides

These are summarised in Table 1.

▼ **Table 1** *The trends in the physical properties of some of the oxides of Period 3 elements*

	Na_2O	MgO	Al_2O_3	SiO_2	P_4O_{10}	SO_3	SO_2
T_m / K	1548	3125	2345	1883	573	290	200
Bonding	ionic	ionic	ionic/covalent	covalent	covalent	covalent	covalent
Structure	giant ionic	giant ionic	giant ionic	giant covalent (macromolecular)	molecular	molecular	molecular

As you go from left to right across the period:

- bonding changes from ionic to covalent
- structure changes from giant ionic through macromolecular to small covalent molecules.

The structures are reflected in the melting points – giant structures have high melting points and molecular structures low ones.

The bonding in aluminium oxide has a significant degree of covalent character. This is because the Al^{3+} ion is small and highly charged and can distort the electron cloud around the O^{2-} ion. This is called polarisation, see Figure 1.

▲ **Figure 1** *Covalency in aluminium oxide*

The reactions of oxides with water

These are summarised in Table 2. There is an overall pattern of alkaline products on the left (metal) side of the Period and acidic products on the right. Aluminium oxide and silicon dioxide are both insoluble in water and do not react.

▼ **Table 2** *The oxides in water*

Oxide	Bonding	Ions present after reaction with water	Acidity/ alkalinity	Approx. pH (Actual values depend on concentration)
Na_2O	ionic	$Na^+(aq)$, $OH^-(aq)$	strongly alkaline	13–14
MgO	ionic	$Mg^{2+}(aq)$, $OH^-(aq)$	somewhat alkaline	10
Al_2O_3	covalent/ ionic	insoluble, no reaction	—	7
SiO_2	covalent	insoluble, no reaction	—	7
P_4O_{10}	covalent	$H^+(aq) + H_2PO_4^-(aq)$	fairly strong acid	1–2
SO_2	covalent	$H^+(aq) + HSO_3^-(aq)$	weak acid	2–3
SO_3	covalent	$H^+(aq) + HSO_4^-(aq)$	strong acid	0–1

The equations are:

$$Na_2O(s) + H_2O(l) \rightarrow 2NaOH(aq) \rightarrow 2Na^+(aq) + 2OH^-(aq)$$

$$MgO(s) + H_2O(l) \rightarrow Mg(OH)_2(aq) \rightleftharpoons Mg^{2+} + 2OH^-(aq)$$

$$P_4O_{10}(s) + 6H_2O(l) \rightarrow 4H_3PO_4(aq) \rightleftharpoons 4H^+(aq) + 4H_2PO_4^-(aq)$$

$$SO_2(g) + H_2O(l) \rightarrow H_2SO_3(aq) \rightleftharpoons H^+(aq) + HSO_3^-(aq) \rightleftharpoons 2H^+(aq) + SO_3^{2-}(aq)$$

$$SO_3(g) + H_2O(l) \rightarrow H_2SO_4(aq) \rightleftharpoons H^+(aq) + HSO_4^-(aq) \rightleftharpoons 2H^+(aq) + SO_4^{2-}(aq)$$

When they dissolve in water, the two ionic compounds first produce O^{2-} ions which are strong bases and react with water to form an alkaline solution.

$$O^{2-} + H_2O \rightarrow 2OH^-$$

The bonding in aluminium oxide ions is too strong for the lattice to dissociate, while silicon dioxide has a giant covalent structure which is not affected by water.

The non-metals produce so-called oxo-acids which dissociate in water to form H^+ ions.

 Go further: The chemistry of mortar

Mortar for bricklaying is essentially a mixture of sand and slaked lime, calcium hydroxide, $Ca(OH)_2$, made into a paste with water. The mortar first sets as the water evaporates. Over time, the calcium hydroxide reacts with carbon dioxide in the air to form calcium carbonate (a hard solid) which binds the bricks together.

$$Ca(OH)_2(s) + CO_2(g) \rightarrow CaCO_3(s) + H_2O(l)$$

a What is the atom economy of this reaction?
b The chemistry of this process is similar to that of a well-known test in school chemistry. Name the test and explain.
   Over time, the calcium carbonate in the hardened mortar reacts with more carbon dioxide and water in the air to form soluble calcium hydrogencarbonate, $Ca(HCO_3)_2$, which may be washed away, so the brickwork needs to be re-pointed.
c Write a balanced equation with state symbols for this process.

Summary questions

1 The $H_2PO_4^-$(aq) ion can dissociate further, losing the remaining two hydrogens as H^+ ions. Write the equations for these reactions. (*4 marks*)

2 Give the oxidation states of each atom in the following equation. Is this a redox reaction? Explain.
   $$Na_2O(s) + H_2O(l) \rightarrow 2NaOH(aq)$$ (*3 marks*)

3 Phosphorus forms another oxide, P_4O_6.
   a Suggest how it might be formed from phosphorus. (*1 mark*)
   b Suggest an equation for its reaction with water. (*2 marks*)

The general trend

The general trend, as in Period 2, is from basic oxides on the left to acidic ones on the right of the Period.

The oxides of sodium and magnesium are basic, while aluminium oxide shows both acidic and basic properties – it is called an amphoteric oxide. Silicon, phosphorus, and sulfur oxides get increasingly acidic. Chlorine forms several oxides which are not considered here – however they are acidic as expected. Argon does not form an oxide.

The basic oxides

The oxides of sodium and magnesium both react with acids to form a salt and water, for example

$Na_2O(s) + 2HCl\ (aq) \rightarrow 2NaCl\ (aq) + H_2O(l)$

$MgO(s) + H_2SO_4(aq) \rightarrow MgSO_4(aq) + H_2O(aq)$

The amphoteric oxide

Aluminium is a metal but it shows some non-metal characteristics.

Aluminium oxide will react with both acids and bases: with hydrochloric acid

$Al_2O_3(s) + 6HCl(aq) \rightarrow 2AlCl_3(aq) + 3H_2O(l)$

and with hot concentrated sodium hydroxide

$Al_2O_3(s) + 2NaOH(l) + 3H_2O \rightarrow 2NaAl(OH)_4(aq)$

The product is sodium aluminate.

The acidic oxides

Silicon dioxide is weakly acidic – it will react with hot, concentrated strong alkalis for example

$SiO_2(s) + 2NaOH(aq) \rightarrow Na_2SiO_3(aq) + 3H_2O(l)$

The product is sodium silicate.

Phosphorus pentoxide first reacts with water to form phosphoric(V) acid, H_3PO_4, which then reacts in stages with an alkali:

The overall reaction is:

$3KOH(aq) + H_3PO_4(aq) \rightarrow K_3PO_4 + H_2O(l)$

Sulfur dioxide reacts with sodium hydroxide to form first sodium hydrogensulfate(IV) and then sodium sulfate(IV):

$SO_2(g) + NaOH(aq) \rightarrow NaHSO_3(aq)$

$NaHSO_3(aq) + NaOH(aq) \rightarrow Na_2SO_3(aq) + H_2O(l)$

Revision tip
An alkali is a soluble base.

Revision tip
Make sure that you can write balanced equations for each oxide reacting with any common acid.

Revision tip
Sodium hydrogensulfate(IV) and sodium sulfate(IV) are often called sodium hydrogensulfite and sodium sulfite respectively.

Summary questions

1 The gas sulfur trioxide, SO_3, also reacts with alkalis. Write a balanced symbol equation with state symbols for its overall reaction with potassium hydroxide.
   (2 marks)

2 Give the oxidation states of each atom in the equation
   $3KOH(aq) + H_3PO_4(aq) \rightarrow K_3PO_4 + 3H_2O(l)$ *(4 marks)*

3 Write balanced symbol equations with state symbols for the reactions of sodium oxide with sulfuric acid and magnesium oxide with hydrochloric acid.
   (4 marks)

1 a Write equations for the reactions that occur when **i** sodium oxide and **ii** sulfur dioxide react with water. Show the ions that are formed.

(4 marks)

b State the trend in the properties of the oxides that this illustrates as you go across Period 3 in the Periodic Table. *(1 mark)*

c Aluminium oxide is described as amphoteric. Explain this term and give equations that illustrate this behaviour. *(5 marks)*

2 An industrial process produces waste containing phosphorus(V) oxide (phosphorus pentoxide, P_4O_{10}). This is reacted with water to form an acidic solution which is neutralised before further disposal.

a Write an equation for the reaction of phosphorus pentoxide with water.

(2 marks)

b The resulting acidic solution is neutralised with excess magnesium oxide.

   i What is meant by 'excess'? *(1 mark)*

   ii Write an equation for this neutralisation. *(2 marks)*

   iii State the oxidation state of each atom in the equation before and after reaction. Is this a redox reaction? *(4 marks)*

c What happens to the excess magnesium oxide and how could it be separated from the neutralised waste water? *(2 marks)*

d Why is this scheme better than using excess sodium hydroxide to neutralise the acid? *(1 mark)*

3 Consider the following oxides of elements in Period 3: Na_2O, MgO, Al_2O_3, SiO_2, P_4O_{10}, SO_3.

a Select one that is amphoteric. *(1 mark)*

b Select two that form acidic solutions in water. *(2 marks)*

c Select one with a giant covalent structure. *(1 mark)*

d Select one that is a gas. *(1 mark)*

e Write an equation for the reaction that happens when **i** Na_2O and **ii** SO_3 react with water. *(4 marks)*

f Write an equation for the reaction that happens when the products of **e i** and **ii** react together. *(2 marks)*

23.1 The general properties of transition metals

Specification reference: 3.2.5

The elements from titanium to copper are called transition metals. They are included in the d-block elements and outlined in Figure 1.

▲ **Figure 1** *The d-block elements [shaded] and the transition metals [outlined]*

The transition elements are all typical metals. Their chemical properties are very similar and this can be explained by their electronic configuration.

What is a transition element?

A transition element forms at least one stable ion with a *part-full* d-shell of electrons.

Not all d-block elements are transition metals. Scandium only forms Sc^{3+} ($3d^0$), and zinc only forms Zn^{2+} ($3d^{10}$) in all their compounds. They are therefore d-block elements but not transition elements.

Figure 2 shows the electron arrangements for the elements in the first row of the d-block.

In general there are two outer 4s electrons and as you go across the period, electrons are added to the *inner* 3d sub-shell. This explains the overall similarity of these elements.

Chromium, Cr, and copper, Cu, have only one electron in the 4s outer shell. In copper, Cu, the d sub-shell is full ($3d^{10}$) and in chromium, Cr, it is half full ($3d^5$), which makes them more stable than expected, but they both can form ions with a part full d-shell.

Chemical properties of transition metals

The chemistry of transition metals has four main features which are common to all the elements:

- Complex formation: A complex ion is formed when a transition metal ion is surrounded by ions or other molecules, collectively called ligands. See Topic 23.2, Complex formation and the shape of complex ions.

- Colour: Most transition metal ions are coloured. See Topic 23.3, Coloured ions.

- Variable oxidation states: They have more than one oxidation state in their compounds. They can therefore take part in many redox reactions. See Topic 23.4, Variable oxidation states of transition elements.

- Catalysis: Many transition metals, and their compounds, show catalytic activity. See 23.5, Catalysts.

		3d	4s
Sc	[Ar] $3d^1 4s^2$	↑□□□□	↑↓
Ti	[Ar] $3d^2 4s^2$	↑↑□□□	↑↓
V	[Ar] $3d^3 4s^2$	↑↑↑□□	↑↓
Cr	[Ar] $3d^5 4s^1$	↑↑↑↑↑	↑
Mn	[Ar] $3d^5 4s^2$	↑↑↑↑↑	↑↓
Fe	[Ar] $3d^6 4s^2$	↑↓↑↑↑↑	↑↓
Co	[Ar] $3d^7 4s^2$	↑↓↑↓↑↑↑	↑↓
Ni	[Ar] $3d^8 4s^2$	↑↓↑↓↑↓↑↑	↑↓
Cu	[Ar] $3d^{10} 4s^1$	↑↓↑↓↑↓↑↓↑↓	↑
Zn	[Ar] $3d^{10} 4s^2$	↑↓↑↓↑↓↑↓↑↓	↑↓

▲ **Figure 2** *The electronic arrangement of the elements in the first transition series. [Ar] represents $1s^2 2s^2 2p^6 3s^2 3p^6$*

Revision tip
When transition metals react to form ions, the 4s electrons are always lost first.

Summary questions

1 Why does the fact that the d-shell is filling after the s-shell mean the transition metals are similar?
(1 mark)

2 **a** Write the full electron configuration for a titanium atom in the form $1s^2$ etc. *(1 mark)*
  b Write the electron configuration of a titanium atom using the shorthand [Ar] etc. *(1 mark)*
  c Write the electron configuration of a Ti^{2+} ion using the shorthand [Ar] etc. *(1 mark)*

3 The electron configuration of the manganese atom is [Ar] $3d^5 4s^2$.
  a Which electrons are removed when a Mn^{2+} ion is formed? *(1 mark)*
  b Suggest why this ion would be expected to be particularly stable.
(1 mark)

23.2 Complex formation and the shape of complex ions

Specification reference: 3.2.5

▲ **Figure 1** *A complex ion of a metal M with co-ordination number 4*

Key terms

Co-ordinate (dative) bond: A covalent bond formed when the pair of electrons comes from the same atom.

Ligand: An ion or molecule that donates a lone pair of electrons to form a co-ordinate bond with a transition metal.

▲ **Figure 2** *Ethane 1,2-diamine (abbreviation en)*

▲ **Figure 3** *The ethanedioate ion*

▲ **Figure 4** *EDTA*

Revision tip
When the ligand is water, the complex ion is called an aqua ion, for example, $[Cu(H_2O)_6]^{2+}(aq)$.

The formation of complex ions

All transition metal ions can accept electrons from ligands to form co-ordinate bonds.

Some examples of ligands are $H_2O:$, $:NH_3$, $:Cl^-$, $:CN^-$

Two, four, or six ligands can bond to a transition metal ion to form a **complex ion**. The number of ligands that surround the metal ion is called the **co-ordination number**.

Multidentate ligands – chelation

Multidentate ligands have more than one atom with a lone pair of electrons which can bond to a transition metal ion. Bidentate ligands have two lone pairs, see Figures 2 and 3.

The ion ethylenediaminetetraacetate, called $EDTA^{4-}$, see Figure 4, can act as a hexadentate ligand.

The resulting complex ions with their multidentate ligands are called **chelates**.

The chelate effect

If you add a hexadentate ligand such as EDTA to a solution of a transition metal salt, the EDTA will replace all six water ligands in an aqua ion such as $[Cu(H_2O)_6]^{2+}$:

$[Cu(H_2O)_6]^{2+}(aq) + EDTA^{4-}(aq) \rightarrow [CuEDTA]^{2-}(aq) + 6H_2O(l)$

The entropy of the system increases from left to right, which is why $[CuEDTA]^{2-}(aq)$ is readily formed.

Haemoglobin

Haemoglobin is a compound of Fe^{2+} complexed with a tetradentate ring ligand, haem, and a protein, globin. A sixth ligand site accepts an oxygen molecule, which is a poor ligand. The complex carries oxygen round the bloodstream, releasing it in the cells. But oxygen can be replaced by carbon monoxide, which is a better ligand, and this prevents the carriage of oxygen.

Shapes and charges of complex ions

- Ions with co-ordination number six are octahedral, for example, $[Co(NH_3)_6]^{3+}$.
- Ions with co-ordination number four are usually tetrahedral, for example, $[CoCl_4]^{2-}$.
- Some ions with co-ordination number four are square planar, for example, $[Ni(CN)_4]^{2-}$.
- Complex ions may have a positive charge or a negative charge.

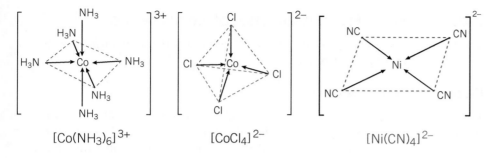

$[Co(NH_3)_6]^{3+}$ $[CoCl_4]^{2-}$ $[Ni(CN)_4]^{2-}$

In $[Co(NH_3)_6]^{3+}$, the metal ion has a charge of +3 and as the NH_3 ligands are all neutral, the complex ion has an overall charge of +3.

In $[CoCl_4]^{2-}$, the metal ion has a charge of +2 and each of the four ligands Cl^- has a charge of −1, so the complex ion has an overall charge of −2.

The reason for the difference in shape is that the chloride ion is a larger ligand than the ammonia molecule, so only four Cl^- ligands can fit around the metal ion, whereas there is room for six NH_3 ligands.

Some complexes are linear – one example is $[Ag(NH_3)_2]^+$:

$[H_3N \rightarrow Ag \leftarrow NH_3]^+$

A solution containing this complex ion is called Tollens' reagent and is used in organic chemistry to distinguish aldehydes from ketones, see Topic 26.2, Reactions of the carbonyl group in aldehydes and ketones.

 Go further: The shape of xenon tetrafluoride

Xenon tetrafluoride, XeF_4, is one of a small number of inert gas compounds. The factors governing their shapes are similar to those for transition metal complexes. The dot-and-cross diagram for XeF_4 is shown.

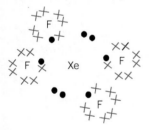

a In XeF_4, the xenon atom has more than eight electrons in its full outer shell. Explain how this can occur.
b How many electrons does the xenon atom have in its outer shell in XeF_4?
c What shape is the XeF_4 molecule based on?
d How many lone pairs are there in the outer shell of the xenon atom in XeF_4?
The structure of XeF_4 is shown.

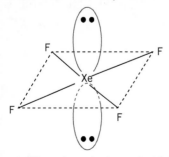

e What shape is the molecule?
f Explain why the lone pairs take up the positions that they do.

▲ **Figure 5** *The cis- or Z- isomer (top) and the trans- or E- isomer (bottom)*

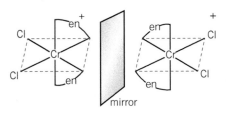

en is an abbreviation for ethane-1,2-diamine:

▲ **Figure 6** *Transition metal complexes that are non-identical mirror images of each other (top) and the structure of the ethane-1,2,-diamine (en) ligand (bottom)*

Isomerism in transition metal complexes

Transition metal complexes can form both geometrical isomers (*cis-trans* or *E-Z* isomers) and optical isomers.

Geometrical isomerism

This occurs in octahedral and square planar complexes. For example in the complex ion $[CrCl_2(H_2O)_4]^+$, the Cl^- ligands may be next to each other (the *cis-* or *Z-* form) or on opposite sides of the central chromium ion (the *trans-* or *E-*form) (Figure 5).

In the square planar complex platin, the Cl^- ligands may be next to each other (the *cis-* or *Z-* form) or on opposite sides of the central platinum atom (the *trans-* or *E-* form).

Optical isomerism

Transition metal complexes exist as pairs of optical isomers if they have two or more bidentate ligands (see Figure 6).

Optical isomers are chiral. They have identical chemical properties but one isomer will rotate the plane of polarisation of polarised light clockwise and the other anticlockwise.

Summary questions

1 $[Cu(H_2O)_6]^{2+}(aq) + EDTA^{4-}(aq) \rightarrow [CuEDTA]^{2-}(aq) + 6H_2O(l)$
   a How many entities are there on each side of the equation? *(1 mark)*
   b Explain why this causes an increase in entropy. *(1 mark)*

2 Explain why carbon monoxide is a poison, even when there may be oxygen present in the air. *(2 marks)*

3 a Which is the larger ligand, NH_3 or Br^-? *(1 mark)*
   b How does this affect the shape of a complex ion? *(2 marks)*

4 This is the structure of a ligand.

   a Suggest which atoms are most likely to form co-ordinate bonds. *(1 mark)*
   b What feature of these atoms allows them to form co-ordinate bonds? *(1 mark)*
   c Is it likely to be a monodentate, bidentate, or hexadentate ligand? *(1 mark)*

23.3 Coloured ions

Specification reference: 3.2.5

Most transition metal compounds are coloured.

If a solution of a substance looks purple, it is because it absorbs all the light from a beam of white light except red and blue. The red and blue light passes through and the solution appears purple, (Figure 1).

Why are transition metal complexes coloured?

- Transition metal compounds have part-filled d-orbitals so electrons are able to move from one d-orbital to another.

- The presence of other atoms nearby means the d-orbitals have slightly different energies.

- Electrons move from one d-orbital to another of a higher energy level (an excited state). As they do so, they absorb energy equal to the difference in energy, ΔE, between levels. This is often in the visible region of the spectrum.

- This colour is therefore missing from the spectrum and you see the combination of the colours that are not absorbed.

ΔE is responsible for the colour of the complex. It depends on the oxidation state of the metal and also on the ligands (and therefore the shape of the complex ion).

$$\Delta E = h\nu = \frac{hc}{\lambda}$$ where ν is frequency, λ is wavelength, c is the velocity of light, and h is Planck's constant.

Table 1 shows examples of how the oxidation state of the metal affects the colour of the complex.

▼ **Table 1**

Oxidation state of metal	2	3
iron complexes	$[Fe(H_2O)_6]^{2+}$ green	$[Fe(H_2O)_6]^{3+}$ pale brown
chromium complexes	$[Cr(H_2O)_6]^{2+}$ blue	$[Cr(H_2O)_6]^{3+}$ red-violet
cobalt complexes	$[Co(NH_3)_6]^{2+}$ brown	$[Co(NH_3)_6]^{3+}$ yellow

Colorimetry

▲ **Figure 2** A simple colorimeter

⚠ You can use a Colorimeter, see Figure 2, to measure the concentration of coloured solutions. The more concentrated the colour, the less light will reach the detector. A suitable filter makes the experiment more sensitive.

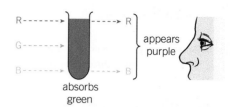

▲ **Figure 1** Solutions look coloured because they absorb some colours and let others pass through

Revision tip

The absorption of visible light is used in spectroscopy.

Summary questions

1 Explain why solutions containing the Sc^{3+} ion are colourless, although scandium is in the d-block. *(1 mark)*

2 Solutions containing V^{3+} ions are green.
   a What colour of light passes through this solution? *(1 mark)*
   b What happens to the other colours of the visible spectrum? *(1 mark)*

3 $[CuCl_4]^{2-}$ is yellow/green whereas $[Cu(NH_3)_6]^{2+}$ is dark blue. Suggest two factors that could be responsible for the difference in colour. *(2 marks)*

23.4 Variable oxidation states of transition elements

Specification reference: 3.2.5

▼ **Table 1** *Zinc ions in acid solution will reduce vanadium(V) through oxidation states V(IV) and V(III) to V(II).*

Oxidation number	Species	Colour
5	$VO_2^+(aq)$	yellow
4	$VO^{2+}(aq)$	blue
3	$V^{3+}(aq)$	green
2	$V^{2+}(aq)$	violet

Revision tip

Remember the phrase OIL RIG – oxidation is loss, reduction is gain (of electrons).

Oxidation states

A typical transition metal can use its 3d electrons as well as its 4s electrons in bonding, and so can have a variety of oxidation states in different compounds. All the transition elements show the +2 oxidation state. These are ions formed by the loss of 4s electrons.

The higher oxidation states are not simple ions. For example, Mn^{7+} ions only exist covalently bonded to oxygen in a compound ion as in MnO_4^-.

Table 1 shows the colour changes when the vanadate(V) ion is reduced.

Redox titrations 🔬

The concentration of an oxidising or a reducing agent can be measured with a redox titration provided we know the equation for the reaction.

Question and model answer: What is the equation for the reaction of MnO_4^- with Fe^{2+}?

During this reaction the oxidation number of the manganese falls from +7 to +2.

Write the half equation for the reduction of Mn(VII) to Mn(II).

1 $MnO_4^-(aq) \rightarrow Mn^{2+}(aq)$

Balance the oxygen atoms using H^+ ions and H_2O molecules.

2 $MnO_4^- + 8H^+(aq) \rightarrow Mn^{2+}(aq) + 4H_2O(l)$

Balance for charge using electrons.

3 $MnO_4^-(aq) + 5e^- + 8H^+(aq) \rightarrow Mn^{2+}(aq) + 4H_2O(l)$

Write the half equation for the oxidation of iron(II) to iron(III).

4 $Fe^{2+}(aq) \rightarrow Fe^{3+}(aq) + e^-$

Multiply the Fe^{2+} / Fe^{3+} half reaction by five (so that the numbers of electrons in each half reaction are the same) and then add the two half equations.

5 $5Fe^{2+}(aq) \rightarrow 5Fe^{3+}(aq) + 5e^-$

$MnO_4^-(aq) + 5e^- + 8H^+(aq) \rightarrow Mn^{2+}(aq) + 4H_2O(l)_5$

- -

$5Fe^{2+}(aq) + MnO_4^-(aq) + \cancel{5e^-} + 8H^+(aq) \rightarrow 5Fe^{3+}(aq) + \cancel{5e^-} + Mn^{2+}(aq) + 4H_2O(l)$

$5Fe^{2+}(aq) + MnO_4^-(aq) + 8H^+(aq) \rightarrow 5Fe^{3+}(aq) + Mn^{2+}(aq) + 4H_2O(l)$

So, $Fe^{2+}(aq)$ reacts with manganate(VII) ions in the ratio 5 : 1.

Cancel out the electrons on each side

The colour of the mixture changes from almost colourless Fe^{2+} to pale pink Mn^{2+} as the reaction proceeds. At the end point, one more drop of $MnO_4^-(aq)$ ions will turn the solution purple. So no indicator is needed for this titration.

Worked example: The reaction between manganate(VII) ions and ethanedioate ions

To find the redox equation use the steps as before

1, 2, and 3 $MnO_4^-(aq) + 8H^+(aq) + 5e^- \rightarrow Mn^{2+}(aq) + 4H_2O(l)$

4 $C_2O_4^{2-}(aq) \rightarrow 2CO_2(g) + 2e^-$

Multiply first equation by 2 and second by 5 to match the number of electrons and then add the two equations together

$2MnO_4^-(aq) + 16H^+(aq) + 5C_2O_4^{2-}(aq) \rightarrow 10CO_2(g) + 2Mn^{2+}(aq) + 8H_2O(l)$

Summary questions

1 In what ratio do $MnO_4^-(aq)$ ions react with $C_2O_4^{2-}(aq)$ ions? (*1 mark*)

2 **a** Add the oxidation states to this equation.
   $2MnO_4^-(aq) + 16H^+(aq) + 5C_2O_4^{2-}(aq) \rightarrow 10CO_2(g) + 2Mn^{2+}(aq) + 8H_2O(l)$
   (*1 mark*)

   b Which atoms have been oxidised and which reduced? (*1 mark*)

3 Use the half equation technique to write a balanced equation for the reduction of VO_2^+ to VO^{2+} by zinc in acid solution.
   $(Zn(s) \rightarrow Zn^{2+}(aq) + 2e^-)$. (*1 mark*)

23.5 Catalysis

Synoptic link

Catalysts and activation energy are introduced in Topic 5.3, Catalysts.

Revision tip

Adsorption means forming weak bonds with a strength somewhere between covalent bonds and van der Waals forces.

Summary questions

1 What steps do you have to go through to deduce the overall equation for the oxidation of sulfur dioxide from the two steps shown above? (*2 marks*)

2 What happens to the oxidation state of the vanadium pentoxide as it catalyses the oxidation of sulfur dioxide? (*2 marks*)

3 **a** Add the two steps of the oxidation of iodide ions to iodine by peroxodisulfate ions to find the overall reaction. (*2 marks*)

   b Select from 'oxidising agent', 'acid', 'reducing agent',' base'. Which term best describes the function of **i** Fe^{2+}, **ii** Fe^{3+}? (*2 marks*)

   c Suggest why the two steps are faster than the uncatalysed reaction. (*2 marks*)

Catalysts lower the activation energy for reactions.

Homogeneous and heterogeneous catalysts

- **Homogeneous catalysts** are in the same phase as the reactants – usually in aqueous solutions.
- **Heterogeneous catalysts** are in a different phase to the reactants – usually a solid catalyst for a gas phase reaction.

Many metal catalysts work at the surface by forming weak bonds with the molecules in a reaction. This is called adsorption. It weakens the bonds in the reactants allowing the reaction to proceed more easily. The metal also holds the reactants in the correct orientation to react. Transition metals use their part-filled d-orbitals to form weak bonds with the reactants. These bonds must be strong enough to hold the reactants but weak enough to release the products.

Catalysts may also work by using the property of a transition metal to have variable oxidation states. For example, vanadium(V) oxide (vanadium pentoxide, V_2O_5) catalyses the oxidation of sulfur dioxide, SO_2, to sulfur trioxide, SO_3, by oxygen in the Contact process for making sulfuric acid. The steps are:

$$SO_2(g) + V_2O_5(s) \rightarrow SO_3(g) + V_2O_4(s)$$

$$2V_2O_4(s) + O_2(g) \rightarrow 2V_2O_5$$

The overall reaction is $2SO_2(g) + O_2(g) \rightarrow 2SO_3(g)$

Examples of heterogeneous catalysts

Iron in the Haber process for making ammonia.

Platinum and rhodium in catalytic converters for car exhaust systems. These convert polluting gases such as carbon monoxides, nitrogen oxides, and hydrocarbons into nitrogen, carbon dioxide, and water.

Examples of homogeneous catalysis

The oxidation of iodide ions to iodine by peroxodisulfate ions, $S_2O_8^{2-}$, catalysed by Fe^{2+} ions.

Step 1: $S_2O_8^{2-}(aq) + 2Fe^{2+}(aq) \rightarrow 2SO_4^{2-}(aq) + 2Fe^{3+}(aq)$

Step 2: $2Fe^{3+}(aq) + 2I^- \rightarrow 2Fe^{2+} + I_2(aq)$

The catalyst is regenerated in step 2.

Autocatalysis

This occurs when a product of the reaction acts as catalyst. The reaction starts slowly and then speeds up once the catalyst is formed. For example, in the following reaction, Mn^{2+} is the catalyst. Once the reaction starts the Mn^{2+} reacts with MnO_4^- ions to form Mn^{3+} as an intermediate species. This then reacts with $C_2O_4^{2-}$ ions to reform Mn^{2+}.

$$2MnO_4^-(aq) + 16H^+(aq) + 5C_2O_4^{2-}(aq) \rightarrow 10CO_2(g) + 2Mn^{2+}(aq) + 8H_2O(l)$$

Chapter 23 Practice questions

1 a Complete the electron arrangement of **i** the Cr^{3+} ion **ii** the Zn^{2+} ion. *(2 marks)*

$1s^2$ ......

b Explain why chromium is considered to be a transition metal and zinc is not. *(1 mark)*

c The complex ion $[CrCl_2(H_2O)_4]^+$ exists as two isomers. One has the structure

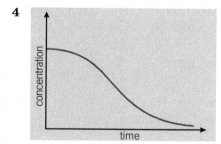

i Draw the structure of the other isomer in the same style. *(1 mark)*

ii What type of isomerism is this? *(1 mark)*

iii Which isomer is the one drawn above? *(1 mark)*

2 a State the shape of the $[Cu(H_2O)_6]^+$ ion and the $CuCl_4^{2-}$ ion. Explain why they have different shapes and different charges. *(6 marks)*

b Predict the shape of the $CuBr_4^{2-}$ ion and explain your reasoning. *(2 marks)*

3 a Complete the electron arrangement of the Cu^{2+} ion starting from [Ar]. *(1 mark)*

b Explain in terms of the d orbitals why the $[Cu(H_2O)_6]^{2+}$ ion is coloured. *(4 marks)*

c i State the meaning of each term in the equation $\Delta E = hv$. **ii** Explain the relevance of this equation to the colour of a transition metal ion. *(4 marks)*

4

The diagram shows a reaction rate curve for a reaction involving transition metal ions.

a What is unusual about the shape of the curve? *(2 marks)*

b Suggest what type of reaction is occurring and describe how this explains the shape of the curve. *(3 marks)*

24.1 The acid–base chemistry of aqueous transition metal ions

Specification reference: 3.2.6

Revision tip

When drawing co-ordinate bonds, the arrow represents the donated pair of electrons.

Transition metals form complexes with ligands. When the ligand is water, metal complexes are called **aqua ions**. For example, $[Cu(H_2O)_6]^{2+}$ is present in copper sulfate solutions, see Topic 23.2, Complex formation and the shape of complex ions.

In a solution of iron(II) nitrate, $Fe(NO_3)_2$, the Fe^{2+} ion exists as the complex ion $[Fe(H_2O)_6]^{2+}$. In a solution of an iron(III) salt the complex formed is $[Fe(H_2O)_6]^{3+}$. These are both octahedral.

▲ **Figure 1** $[Fe(H_2O)_6]^{2+}$ (left) and $[Fe(H_2O)_6]^{3+}$ (right)

The acidity of metal aqua ions in aqueous solution

Revision tip

The *smaller* the value of pK_a, the *stronger* the acid.

With transition metals, M^{3+} (aq) ions are more acidic than M^{2+} (aq) ions. For example, Fe^{2+}(aq) solutions are not noticeably acidic, but those of Fe^{3+}(aq) ($pK_a = 2.2$) are stronger acids than ethanoic acid ($pK_a = 4.8$).

The Fe^{3+} ion is both smaller and more highly charged than Fe^{2+} and strongly attracts electrons from the oxygen atoms of the water ligands and this weakens the O—H bonds. The complex ion will then release a H^+ ion making the solution acidic (Figure 2). Fe^{2+} is less polarising and so fewer O—H bonds break in solution.

$$[Fe(H_2O)_6]^{3+}(aq) \rightleftharpoons [Fe(H_2O)_5(OH)]^{2+}(aq) + H^+(aq)$$

Summary questions

1 Why are transition metals M^{3+} (aq) ions more acidic that M^{2+} (aq) ions?
   (1 mark)

2 **a** What would you expect to see if sodium carbonate is added to a solution containing iron(III) aqua ions?
   (1 mark)
   b Explain your answer.
   (1 mark)

3 Explain why the *smaller* the value of pKa, the *stronger* the acid.
   (2 marks)

electrons attracted

pale violet

yellow

▲ **Figure 2** The acidity of Fe^{3+}(aq) ions

Amphoteric hydroxides

Amphoteric means showing both acidic and basic properties.

Aluminium hydroxide, $Al(H_2O)_3(OH)_3$, is amphoteric. For example, with hydrochloric acid it acts as a base:

$$Al(H_2O)_3(OH)_3 + 3HCl \rightarrow Al(H_2O)_6^{3+} + 3Cl^-$$

But aluminium hydroxide, like Fe^{3+}, has a small and highly charged metal ion and will react with the base sodium hydroxide to give a colourless solution of sodium tetrahydroxoaluminate:

$$Al(H_2O)_3(OH)_3 + OH^- \rightarrow [Al(OH)_4]^- + 3H_2O$$

That is, is acting as an acid.

24.2 Ligand substitution reactions
24.3 A summary of acid–base and substitution reactions of some metal ions

Specification reference: 3.2.6

Some test tube reactions of metal ions 🧪

The products of many of the reactions of transition metal compounds can be identified by their colours. Table 1 and Table 2 show a number of examples of reactions of metal ions with different bases. The effect of adding the base shown on the left to solutions of aqua ions is shown in the following tables.

▼ **Table 1** *Adding bases to M^{2+}(aq) complexes*

	$[Fe(H_2O)_6]^{2+}$(aq) pale green	$[Cu(H_2O)_6]^{2+}$(aq) pale blue
OH^- little	green gelatinous ppt of $[Fe(H_2O)_4(OH)_2]$*	pale blue ppt of $[Cu(H_2O)_4(OH)_2]$
OH^- excess	green gelatinous ppt of $[Fe(H_2O)_4(OH)_2]$*	pale blue ppt of $[Cu(H_2O)_4(OH)_2]$
NH_3 little	green gelatinous ppt of $[Fe(H_2O)_4(OH)_2]$*	pale blue ppt of $[Cu(H_2O)_4(OH)_2]$
NH_3 excess	green gelatinous ppt of $[Fe(H_2O)_4(OH)_2]$*	deep blue solution of $[Cu(NH_3)_4(H_2O)_2]^{2+}$
CO_3^{2-}	green ppt of $FeCO_3$	blue-green ppt of $CuCO_3$

*Pale green $[Fe(H_2O)_4(OH)_2]$ is soon oxidised by air to brown $[Fe(H_2O)_3(OH)_3]$

In most cases the solid metal hydroxide is precipitated $[M(H_2O)_4(OH)_2]$. Ammonia is also a base *and* a good ligand and, in the case of copper, the copper hydroxide dissolves in excess ammonia forming the deep blue ion $[Cu(NH_3)_4(H_2O)_2]^{2+}$ by a ligand substitution reaction. Precipitates of the metal carbonates form when carbonate ions are added.

▼ **Table 2** *Adding bases to M^{3+}(aq) complexes*

	$[Fe(H_2O)_6]^{3+}$(aq) purple/yellow/brown	$[Al(H_2O)_6]^{3+}$(aq) colourless
OH^- little	brown gelatinous ppt of $[Fe(H_2O)_3(OH)_3]$	white ppt of $[Al(H_2O)_3(OH)_3]$
OH^- excess	brown gelatinous ppt of $[Fe(H_2O)_3(OH)_3]$	colourless solution of $[Al(OH)_4]^-$
NH_3 little	brown gelatinous ppt of $[Fe(H_2O)_3(OH)_3]$	white ppt of $[Al(H_2O)_3(OH)_3]$
NH_3 excess	brown gelatinous ppt of $[Fe(H_2O)_3(OH)_3]$	white ppt of $[Al(H_2O)_3(OH)_3]$
CO_3^{2-}	brown gelatinous ppt of $[Fe(H_2O)_3(OH)_3]$ and bubbles of CO_2	white ppt of $[Al(H_2O)_3(OH)_3]$ and bubbles of CO_2

In the case of the M^{3+} ions, bubbles of carbon dioxide are produced rather than the solid carbonate. This is because $[M(H_2O)_6]^{3+}$ is more acidic than $[M(H_2O)_6]^{2+}$, see Topic 24.1, The acid–base chemistry of aqueous transition metal ions.

Summary questions

1 Write an equation for copper hydroxide dissolving in ammonia solution. (*2 marks*)

2 Explain why solid $FeCO_3$ exists, but solid $Fe_2(CO_3)_3$ does not. (*1 mark*)

3 Give the electron arrangement of Al^{3+} in the form $1s^2$ etc. and use it to explain why aluminium compounds are colourless. (*2 marks*)

1   Adding a solution of sodium carbonate to a solution containing aqueous Fe^{2+} ions produces a green precipitate. Adding a solution of sodium carbonate to a solution containing aqueous Fe^{3+} ions produces a brown precipitate and bubbles of a gas.

   a Identify the products *(2 marks)*

   b Explain the difference between the behaviour of Fe^{3+} and Fe^{2+} ions.
(2 marks)

   c Give appropriate equations. *(6 marks)*

2   **a** Explain the term **chelate**. *(1 mark)*

   b The ligand $EDTA^{4-}$ is a hexadentate ligand. Write an equation to show how $EDTA^{4-}$ can replace the H_2O ligands in the ion $[Cu(H_2O)_6]^{2+}$. *(2 marks)*

   c How many entities are there on **i** the left and **ii** the right of the equation? *(2 marks)*

   d Explain why this means the reaction goes to completion. *(2 marks)*

3   Consider the following reactions.

               Conc. HCl

$$[Cu(H_2O)_6]^{2+}(aq) \quad \rightarrow \quad A \quad (1)$$

$$[Cu(H_2O)_6]^{2+} \rightarrow \text{blue-green precipitate B} \quad (2)$$

$$[Cu(H_2O)_6]^{2+} \rightarrow \text{pale blue precipitate C} \rightarrow [Cu(NH_3)_6]^{2+}(aq) \quad (3)$$

   a Give the formula of the complex ion A. *(1 mark)*

   b **i** Identify B and **ii** suggest a reagent for this reaction. *(2 marks)*

   c **i** Give the formula of C, and **ii** describe the appearance of $[Cu(NH_3)_6]^{2+}(aq)$. *(2 marks)*

   d **i** What reagent converts C to $[Cu(NH_3)_6]^{2+}(aq)$? **ii** What type of reaction is this? *(2 marks)*

   e What is the oxidation state of copper throughout these reactions?
(1 mark)

25.1 Naming organic compounds

Specification reference: 3.3.1

The IUPAC system

The IUPAC system for naming organic compounds is based on a **root** giving the length of the longest hydrocarbon chain with suffixes (and sometimes prefixes) indicating the **functional groups**. Locants are numbers showing where on the longest chain the functional groups (or hydrocarbon side chains) are found. Table 1 includes all the functional groups you will meet.

Synoptic link

The IUPAC system was introduced in Topic 11.1, Carbon compounds.

▼ **Table 1** *The suffixes and prefixes of some functional groups*

Family	Formula	Suffix	Prefix	Example
alkenes	RCH=CH$_2$	-ene		propene, CH$_3$CHCH$_2$
alkynes	RC≡CH	-yne		propyne, CH$_3$CCH
halogenoalkanes	R—X (X is F, Cl, Br, or I)		halo- (fluoro-, chloro-, bromo-, iodo-)	chloromethane, CH$_3$Cl
carboxylic acids	RCOOH	-oic acid		ethanoic acid, CH$_3$COOH
anhydrides	RCOOCOR′	-anhydride		ethanoic anhydride, CH$_3$COOCOCH$_3$
esters	RCOOR′	-oate (Esters are named from their parent alcohol and acid, so propyl ethanoate is derived from propanol and ethanoic acid.)		propyl ethanoate, CH$_3$COOC$_3$H$_7$
acyl chlorides	RCOCl	-oyl chloride		ethanoyl chloride, CH$_3$COCl
amides	RCONH$_2$	-amide		ethanamide, CH$_3$CONH$_2$
nitriles	RC≡N	-nitrile		ethanenitrile, CH$_3$C≡N
aldehydes	RCHO	-al		ethanal, CH$_3$CHO
ketones	RCOR′	-one		propanone, CH$_3$COCH$_3$
alcohols	ROH	-ol	hydroxy-	ethanol, C$_2$H$_5$OH 2-hydroxyethanal, HOCH$_2$CHO
amines	RNH$_2$	-amine	amino-	ethylamine, CH$_3$CH$_2$NH$_2$
arenes	C$_6$H$_5$R			methylbenzene, C$_6$H$_5$CH$_3$

Summary questions

1 Name the following:

(*1 mark each*)

2 Draw **i** the displayed structures and **ii** the skeletal structures of the following:

a propanoic aid   b but-2-ene   c but-1-ene.   (*2 marks each*)

25.2 Optical isomerism

Specification reference: 3.3.7

Optical isomerism is a particular form of **stereoisomerism**.

Chirality

Optical isomerism occurs when two molecules have the same formula but are non-superimposable mirror images of each other.

Such molecules are described as **chiral** (handed).

Optical isomers have a carbon atom that is bonded to four different atoms or groups of atoms.

▲ **Figure 1** *The optical isomers of bromochlorofluoromethane*

This atom is called the **chiral centre** and is usually indicated with an asterisk.

It is much easier to see the chiral centre in the displayed formula, which shows all bonds and all atoms. For example the compound pentan-2-ol has the structural formula $CH_3CH_2CH_2CH(OH)CH_3$, the skeletal formula and the displayed formula.

▲ **Figure 2** *The optical isomers of 2-hydroxypropanoic acid*

Optical isomers can *only* be distinguished on paper using 3-D conventions, for example, wedge bonds coming out of and dotted bonds going into the paper as in Figure 1.

Each isomer rotates the plane of polarisation of polarised light in opposite directions, see Figure 2.

▲ **Figure 3** *Measuring the rotation of the plane of polarisation of polarised light*

The + isomer rotates the plane of polarisation clockwise and the − isomer rotates it anticlockwise.

Summary questions

1 Which of the following molecules show optical isomerism? $CHFCl_2$; CF_3Cl; CF_2Cl_2; CHFClBr. Explain.
   (2 marks)

2 Mark the chiral centre on the following molecule and draw its optical isomer using the same notation. *(2 marks)*

3 α-Amino acids have the formula $RHC(CO_2)(NH_2)$ where R may be H, CH_3, C_2H_5, etc. Give the formula of the *only* α-amino acid that is *not* chiral. Explain your answer. *(2 marks)*

25.3 Synthesis of optically active compounds

Specification reference: 3.3.7

Most chemical reactions that produce optically active compounds produce a 50:50 mixture of the two isomers. This is called a **racemate** (pronounced rass-em-ate) or a **racemic** mixture. The mixture is not optically active because the optical rotations of the two isomers are in opposite directions and cancel each other out. An example of this is the synthesis of 2-hydroxypropanoic acid (lactic acid) from ethanal.

Synthesis of 2-hydroxypropanoic acid (lactic acid) from ethanal

The ethanal molecule is flat and therefore not optically active.

Step 1 addition of hydrogen cyanide

ethanal   2-hydroxypropanenitrile

▲ **Figure 1** The :CN⁻ ion may attack from above or below the molecule

The key step is the attack of $:CN^-$ on $C^{\delta+}$. This is equally likely to happen from above or below, see Figure 1. Each mode of attack will produce a different optical isomer because tetrahedral products are formed.

Step 2 hydrolysis

The nitrile group is converted to a carboxylic acid.

This does not affect chirality so two optical isomers of 2-hydroxypropanoic acid are formed, see Figure 2.

▲ **Figure 2** The two optical isomers of lactic acid: + on the left and − on the right

Summary questions

1 Does the reaction of propanone, below, with hydrogen cyanide produce an optically active product? Explain your answer. *(2 marks)*

2 Explain why pairs of optical isomers have identical boiling and melting points. *(2 marks)*

3

  a Identify the chiral centre in the structure of the drug ibuprofen above. *(1 mark)*
  b Suggest a problem that chirality might cause in a drug. *(1 mark)*

1 The skeletal formula of the drug thalidomide is shown.

    a Thalidomide is chiral. Explain the term chiral.   *(2 marks)*

    b What problems can chirality cause with a drug molecule?   *(2 marks)*

    c Mark the chiral centre on your drawing.   *(1 mark)*

    d Explain how you identified the chiral centre. Hint - it may help to draw in the hydrogen atoms that are not shown in the skeletal formula.   *(1 mark)*

2 Name and write the shorthand structural formula of the following:

    (6 marks)

    a

    b

    c

3 The structure of the amino acid alanine is shown.

    a How long is the longest unbranched chain of carbon atoms?   *(1 mark)*

    b What is the root of the systematic (IUPAC) name of alanine?   *(1 mark)*

    c Where on the carbon chain is the $-NH_2$ (amino) group?   *(1 mark)*

    d State the systematic name of alanine.   *(1 mark)*

    e What type of isomerism does alanine show?   *(1 mark)*

    f How may these isomers be distinguished from each other?   *(1 mark)*

The carbonyl group

The carbonyl group is a carbon–oxygen double bond, C=O.

It is found in aldehydes, RCHO, and ketones, RR'CO.

The simplest aldehyde is methanal,

$$\text{H} \diagdown \text{C}=\text{O}$$
$$\text{H} \diagup$$

where R=H, followed by ethanal,

$$\text{H}_3\text{C} \diagdown \text{C}=\text{O}$$
$$\text{H} \diagup$$

,where R=CH$_3$.

The simplest ketone is propanone

$$\text{H}_3\text{C} \diagdown \text{C}=\text{O}$$
$$\text{H}_3\text{C} \diagup$$

Naming carbonyl compounds

Aldehydes have the suffix –al and ketones the suffix –one.

Aldehydes can only occur at the end of a chain.

Ketones may need a locant to indicate where the C=O group is in a chain, for example, pentan-2-one and pentan-3-one.

Physical properties

The carbonyl group is polarised C$^{\delta+}$=O$^{\delta-}$. So there are strong permanent dipole–dipole forces between the molecules of aldehydes and ketones.

The reactivity of carbonyl compounds

Because of the polarity of the carbonyl group, **nucleophiles** can attack the C$^{\delta+}$.

The C=O is unsaturated so addition reactions are possible.

The typical reactions of carbonyl compounds are **nucleophilic addition reactions**.

Carbonyl compounds can also be oxidised or reduced by suitable oxidising agents or reducing agents.

Summary questions

1 Which carbonyl compound is most likely to be a gas at room temperature? Explain. *(2 marks)*

2 Explain why there are hydrogen bonds between propanone molecules and water molecules but not between propanone molecules themselves. *(2 marks)*

3 a Draw the structural formula of pentan-3-one. *(1 mark)*
   b State the IUPAC name of *(1 mark)*

$$\text{H}-\overset{\displaystyle H}{\underset{\displaystyle H}{\overset{|}{\underset{|}{C}}}}-\overset{\displaystyle H}{\underset{\displaystyle H}{\overset{|}{\underset{|}{C}}}}-\overset{\displaystyle H}{\underset{\displaystyle H}{\overset{|}{\underset{|}{C}}}}-\overset{\displaystyle H}{\underset{\displaystyle H}{\overset{|}{\underset{|}{C}}}}-\text{C}\diagup^{\text{O}}_{\text{H}}$$

26.2 Reactions of the carbonyl group in aldehydes and ketones

Specification reference: 3.3.8

The typical reactions of the carbonyl group are nucleophilic addition and redox.

Nucleophilic addition reactions

The general reaction is

The nucleophile adds on to the $C^{\delta+}$, and a hydrogen atom (from the solvent) adds on to the $O^{\delta-}$. In the reaction with CN^- ions the products, called hydroxynitriles, have one extra carbon atom than the starting materials. Hydroxynitriles can be easily converted into other functional groups.

Redox reactions

Aldehydes can be oxidised to carboxylic acids and reduced to primary alcohols. Ketones cannot be oxidised easily but can be reduced to secondary alcohols.

Oxidation

The oxidising agent is acidified potassium dichromate solution ($H^+/Cr_2O_7^{2-}$). This is yellow but it is reduced to green Cr^{3+} ions as the reaction proceeds. For example, $RCHO + [O] \rightarrow RCOOH$

Reduction

Sodium tetrahydridoborate(III) (sodium borohydride, $NaBH_4$) is used in aqueous solution to reduce aldehydes and ketones to alcohols. It generates the nucleophile $:H^-$, and the mechanism of the reaction is the same as nucleophilic addition. For an aldehyde:

Using [H] to represent the reducing agent the equation is:

Distinguishing aldehydes from ketones

Two tests may be used. Warming an aldehyde with Tollens' reagent, $Ag(NH_3)_2^+$, forms a silver mirror on the test tube as Ag^+ is reduced to Ag. Ketones give no reaction. Warming an aldehyde with Fehling's, or Benedict's, solution turns the blue solution brick red as the Cu^{2+} ions they contain are reduced to Cu^+. Ketones give no reaction. Both depend on the fact that aldehydes are easily oxidised and ketones are not.

Revision tip

It is best to remember the general reaction and apply it to different nucleophiles rather than to memorise all the reactions.

Revision tip

'Curly arrows' show the movement of pairs of electrons. They move from negatively charged areas towards positively charged areas on molecules.

Revision tip

The reagent used to generate CN^- ions is a mixture of KCN and acid. The CN^- ion is very toxic.

Revision tip

It is acceptable to use [O] to represent an oxidising agent, but your equation *must* balance.

Revision tip

It is acceptable to use [H] to represent a reducing agent, but your equation *must* balance.

Summary questions

1 Explain why $:H^-$ is a nucleophile. *(1 mark)*

2 Suggest why tetrahydridoborate(III) will not reduce C=C. *(1 mark)*

3 Write the mechanism for the reduction of a ketone with $:H^-$. *(3 marks)*

26.3 Carboxylic acids and esters
26.4 Reactions of carboxylic acids and esters
Specification reference: 3.3.9

Carboxylic acids have the general formula RCOOH and esters RCOOR'.

A carboxylic acid   An ester

They both contain the carbonyl group C=O whose properties are modified when adjacent to an –OH group or an –OR group. Esters are derivatives of carboxylic acids where an R' group replaces the hydrogen atom of the OH group of the parent acid.

Naming carboxylic acids

Carboxylic acids have the suffix –oic acid, for example CH_3COOH is ethanoic acid. The carboxylic acid can only occur at the end of a chain so locants are not needed. If there are other groups attached to the main chain we count from the carbon of the carboxylic acid.

Naming esters

Esters are named from the parent acid so all esters based on ethanoic acid are called ethanoates. The name of the R group is placed first, see examples.

methyl ethanoate   *ethyl methanoate*

The reactivity of carboxylic acids

Carboxylic acids are polarised as shown:

- The carbonyl carbon is more strongly polarised δ+ than in aldehydes and ketones due to the second oxygen atom bonded to it. So it is easily attacked by nucleophiles.

- The $O^{\delta-}$ of the carbonyl group may be attacked by positively charged reagents such as H^+.

- The $H^{\delta+}$ may be lost as H^+ ion (a proton). In this case the compound is acting as an acid.

Acidic behaviour

Loss of a proton results in a **carboxylate ion** in which the negative charge is spread over three atoms.

This **delocalisation** makes the ions particularly stable, so carboxylic acids are acidic.

Carboxylic acids are weak acids. They will react with sodium hydrogencarbonate to give off carbon dioxide as well as the usual reactions of acids to form salts.

$$RCOOH(aq) + NaHCO_3(aq) \rightarrow RCOO^- Na^+(aq) + CO_2(g) + H_2O(l)$$

Formation of esters

Carboxylic acids react with alcohols, using a strong acid catalyst, to form esters. This is a reversible reaction.

> **Revision tip**
> Make sure you can write balanced equations for the reaction of a carboxylic acid with an alkali, a metal, a metal oxide, and a metal carbonate.

$$R-\underset{\substack{|\\O-R'}}{\overset{\substack{O\\||}}{C}} + H_2O \xrightarrow{\text{H}^+ \text{catalyst}} R-\underset{\substack{|\\O-H}}{\overset{\substack{O\\||}}{C}} + R'-O-H$$

ester   carboxylic acid   alcohol

The reverse of this reaction is called acid **hydrolysis** of the ester.

Revision tip
Catalysts affect the rate of reversible reactions but not the position of equilibrium.

Hydrolysis of esters is also catalysed by bases such as sodium hydroxide. This produces the salt of the acid which removes the acid from the reaction mixture so this reaction goes to completion.

$$CH_3-\underset{\substack{|\\O-CH_3}}{\overset{\substack{O\\||}}{C}} + H_2O \xrightleftharpoons{\text{catalyst}} CH_3-\underset{\substack{|\\OH}}{\overset{\substack{O\\||}}{C}} + CH_3OH \xrightarrow{\text{NaOH}} CH_3-\underset{\substack{|\\O^- + Na^+ + H_2O}}{\overset{\substack{O\\||}}{C}}$$

sodium ethanoate

The mechanism for this reaction can be explained using 'curly arrows'.

Uses of esters

Common uses of esters include solvents, plasticisers, perfumes, and food flavourings.

Vegetable oils and animal fats are esters of propane-1,2,3-triol (glycerol) with long-chain carboxylic acids. They can be hydrolysed by alkalis to make soaps, see Figure 1.

▲ **Figure 1** *The hydrolysis of vegetable oil. R is a long hydrocarbon chain, approximately C_{16}*

Biodiesel is produced by reacting vegetable oils with methanol in the presence of a catalyst to form a mixture of methyl esters of the carboxylic acids that make up the oils.

Summary questions

1 Draw the structural formula of ethyl ethanoate. *(1 mark)*

2 Name

$$H-\underset{\substack{|\\H}}{\overset{\substack{Br\\|}}{C}}-\underset{\substack{|\\H}}{\overset{\substack{H\\|}}{C}}-\overset{\substack{O\\\\\\OH}}{C}$$

(1 mark)

3 What acid and what alcohol would react together to give methyl propanoate? *(2 marks)*

4 What would be the products of hydrolysis of ethyl butanoate catalysed by **a** hydrochloric acid, **b** sodium hydroxide? *(4 marks)*

➕ Go further: Printer inks

Ink jet printer inks need two contrasting properties. They need to be water-soluble while in the cartridge so that they can be sprayed onto the paper, and they need to be insoluble when on the paper so that they do not run. This dilemma is solved by the following equilibrium:

$$RCOO^- (aq) + H^+ (aq) \rightleftharpoons RCOOH(s)$$

RCOOH represents a long-chain carboxylic acid which is coloured and not water-soluble. It is present in the cartridge as its sodium salt, RCOONa, which is water-soluble.

a Write an equation for the dissociation of RCOONa into ions.
   Paper is somewhat acidic – that is, it contains H^+ ions.
b What happens to the following equilibrium when $RCOO^-$ ions are in contact with the paper?
   $$RCOO^-(aq) + H^+(aq) \rightleftharpoons RCOOH(s)$$
c Explain why a long-chain carboxylic acid is insoluble in water while its sodium salt is soluble.

26.5 Acylation

Specification reference: 3.3.9

Acylation is the substitution of the **acyl group**, $R-C\overset{O}{\diagdown}$ into another molecule.

Acid derivatives contain the acyl group and have the general formula:

$$R-C\underset{Z}{\overset{O}{\diagup}}$$

Acid derivatives

Acid derivatives are summarised in Table 1.

▼ **Table 1** *Some acid derivatives*

−Z	Name	General formula	Example
−OR'	ester	RCOOR'	ethyl ethanoate $CH_3COOC_2H_5$
−Cl	acid chloride	RCOCl	ethanoyl chloride CH_3COCl
−OCOR'	acid anhydride	RCOOCOR'	ethanoic anhydride $CH_3COOCOCH_3$
−NH$_2$	amide	RCONH$_2$	ethanamide CH_3CONH_2

Nucleophilic addition–elimination reactions

In all acid derivatives the carbonyl carbon is polarised $C^{\delta+}$ because it is bonded to an electronegative oxygen atom. This $C^{\delta+}$ will be attacked by nucleophiles, followed by loss of: Z^- – the **leaving group**:

$$R-\underset{Z}{\overset{\overset{\delta-}{O}}{C^{\delta+}}} + \;:Nu^- \longrightarrow R-\underset{Nu}{\overset{O}{C}} + \;:Z^-$$

The speed of the reaction is governed by:

- The size of the δ+ charge of the carbonyl carbon which depends on the electron-attracting power of Z.
- How easily Z is lost (how good a leaving group it is).
- How good the nucleophile is.

Nucleophiles

Typical nucleophiles include

$$\underset{\text{primary amine}}{\overset{H}{\underset{H}{:N}}-R} \; > \; \underset{\text{ammonia}}{\overset{H}{\underset{H}{:N}}-H} \; > \; \underset{\text{alcohol}}{\overset{H}{\underset{R}{:O}}} \; > \; \underset{\text{water}}{\overset{H}{\underset{H}{:O}}}$$

The reactions are summarised in Table 2.

▼ **Table 2** *Products of the reactions of acid derivatives with nucleophiles*

←——increasing reactivity

A typical mechanism is shown for ethanoyl chloride and water.

Notice that as the nucleophile (water) is neutral and the leaving group is negatively charged, a H^+ ion must be lost in the final step.

The overall reaction is

$$CH_3COCl + H_2O \rightarrow CH_3OOH + HCl$$

Aspirin

Aspirin is made by acylating 2-hydroxybenzoic acid with ethanoic anhydride:

An alternative acylating agent is ethanoyl chloride but the anhydride is used because it is:

- cheaper
- less corrosive
- produces a safer by-product – ethanoic acid rather than hydrochloric acid.

Summary questions

1 Write the balanced equation for the reaction of ethanol with ethanoyl chloride. (*2 marks*)

2 Suggest why $:NH_3$ is a better nucleophile than $:OH_2$. (*2 marks*)

3 Calculate the atom economy of the reaction used to prepare aspirin. (*2 marks*)

1 a State the IUPAC name of the following:

  i

  $$H-\underset{\underset{H}{|}}{\overset{\overset{H}{|}}{C}}-\underset{\underset{H}{|}}{\overset{\overset{H}{|}}{C}}-\underset{\underset{H}{|}}{\overset{\overset{H}{|}}{C}}-\underset{\underset{H}{|}}{\overset{\overset{H}{|}}{C}}-C\overset{\nearrow O}{\underset{\searrow H}{}}$$

  ii

  $$H_3C-\underset{\underset{H}{|}}{\overset{\overset{H}{|}}{C}}-\overset{\overset{O}{\|}}{C}-\underset{\underset{H}{|}}{\overset{\overset{H}{|}}{C}}-CH_3$$

  iii

  $$H-\underset{\underset{H}{|}}{\overset{\overset{H}{|}}{C}}-\underset{\underset{H}{|}}{\overset{\overset{H}{|}}{C}}-C\overset{\nearrow O}{\underset{\searrow H}{}}$$

  (3 marks)

  b Which two are a pair of isomers? *(1 mark)*

  c Which two are aldehydes? *(2 marks)*

  d Which one is not easily oxidised? *(1 mark)*

  e Which one can be reduced to a secondary alcohol? *(1 mark)*

  f Name a reducing agent that would reduce all three. *(1 mark)*

  g Which two can be oxidised to carboxylic acids? *(2 marks)*

2 a i Draw the displayed formula of butanone.

  ii Why is no locant needed in its name? *(2 marks)*

3 a What are the products of the acid hydrolysis of **i** ethyl methanoate, **ii** methyl ethanoate? *(4 marks)*

  b How would the products differ if a catalyst of sodium hydroxide were used? *(1 mark)*

  c Write an equation for **i** the acid hydrolysis of ethyl methanoate and **ii** the hydrolysis of methyl ethanoate catalysed by sodium hydroxide. *(4 marks)*

4 a Write a balanced equation for the reduction of ethanal to ethanol by sodium tetrahydridoborate(III) (sodium borohydride) using [H] to represent the reducing agent. *(1 mark)*

  b Explain why this reducing agent will reduce compounds containing C=O but not those containing C=C. *(2 marks)*

27.1 Introduction to arenes

Specification reference: 3.3.10

Bonding and structure of benzene

Aromatic compounds are based on benzene, C_6H_6, which is a regular, flat hexagonal ring of carbon atoms, each one bonded to a single hydrogen atom. Although it is unsaturated, it does not usually undergo addition reactions. The bond lengths are all the same and are intermediate between C–C and C=C. Benzene has the special symbol

 which is a shorthand for

The skeleton of the ring is formed from C–C single bonds but each carbon has a p-orbital containing one electron, Figure 1.

▲ **Figure 1** *The p-orbitals in benzene*

These orbitals overlap to form a **delocalised system** of electrons above and below the ring, see Figure 2.

This electron-rich area accounts for much of the chemistry of benzene.

▲ **Figure 2** *Delocalisation in benzene*

The stability of benzene

Benzene is thermochemically much more stable than would be expected if it were 1,3,5-cyclohexatriene, ⬡.

The experimental enthalpy change of hydrogenation of cyclohexene is $-120\,kJ\,mol^{-1}$.

⬡ $+H_2 \rightarrow$ ⬡ $\Delta H = -120\ kJ\ mol^{-1}$

So we would expect that the value for 1,3,5-cyclohexatriene would be three times this, that is, $-360\,kJ\,mol^{-1}$.

The experimental value for benzene is $-208\,kJ\,mol^{-1}$ indicating that benzene is $152\,kJ\,mol^{-1}$ more stable than expected, see Figure 3.

▲ **Figure 3** *Enthalpy diagram for the hydrogenation of 1,3,5-cyclohexatriene, cyclohexane, and benzene*

Common misconception

Do not confuse hydrogenation (reaction with hydrogen) with hydration (reaction with water).

Summary questions

1   Suggest the expected value for the enthalpy of hydrogenation of 1,3-cyclohexadiene. *(1 mark)*

2   The bond length of C–C is 0.154 nm and that of C=C is 0.134 nm. Predict the carbon–carbon bond length in benzene. *(1 mark)*

3   Write a balanced equation for the hydrogenation of benzene. *(1 mark)*

27.2 Arenes – physical properties, naming, and reactivity
27.3 Reactions of arenes
Specification reference: 3.3.10

Benzene is non-polar and mixes well with hydrocarbon solvents but will not dissolve in water. It is a liquid at room temperature.

Naming arenes

Substituted arenes are named as derivatives of benzene with locants to define the positions on the ring where there are two or more of them. Here are some examples:

Methylbenzene   1,2-dichlorobenzene   1,4-dichlorobenzene

Some exceptions include:

phenol   benzoic acid (benzenecarboxylic acid)

The reactivity of arenes

• The aromatic system is very stable and is rarely destroyed in reactions. So the typical reactions of arenes are substitutions.

• The aromatic ring has a high electron density and is attacked by electrophiles.

So the reactions of arenes are typically **electrophilic substitutions**.

Electrophilic substitution reactions of arenes
Mechanism

The general mechanism is

This is the general equation for electrophilic substitution. Notice that a H⁺ ion is lost from the benzene ring and replaced by the electrophile El⁺.

Nitration

The electrophile is NO_2^+, produced in a mixture of concentrated nitric and sulfuric acids:

$$H_2SO_4 + HNO_3 \rightarrow H_2NO_3^+ + HSO_4^- \rightarrow NO_2^+ + HSO_4^- + H_2O$$

The product is nitrobenzene. Further reaction produces small amounts of 1,2-dinitrobenzene and 1,4-dinitrobenzene.

Nitrobenzene can be reduced using tin and hydrochloric acid to phenylamine, . Phenylamine and other substituted aromatic amines are important starting materials for dyestuffs.

Friedel–Crafts acylation

The electrophile is RCO^+, generated from an acyl chloride and an aluminium chloride catalyst:

$$RCOCl + AlCl_3 \rightarrow RCO^+ + AlCl_4^-$$

The product is an acyl-substituted arene .

The balanced equation is

+ RCOCl → + HCl

Synoptic link

Here sulfuric acid is the stronger acid and donates a H^+ ion to nitric acid, see Topic 21.1, Defining an acid.

Summary questions

1 Name and draw the structure of the third isomer of 1,2-dichlorobenzene and 1,4-dichlorobenzene. *(2 marks)*

2 Write the equation for **a** the nitration of benzene with the electrophile NO_2^+. **b** the reduction of nitrobenzene to phenylamine by hydrogen. *(4 marks)*

3 Explain how the catalyst $AlCl_3$ is regenerated in the reaction of RCO^+ with benzene. *(2 marks)*

4 What is the functional group of , which is produced by the reaction of CH_3COCl with benzene? *(1 mark)*

Chapter 27 Practice questions

1 **a** State the IUPAC name of the following:

    i

    ii

    iii

                                                                      (3 marks)

  b Which two are a pair of isomers? *(1 mark)*

  c Draw the structure of 1,2-dimethylbenzene. *(1 mark)*

2 Explain why the reactions of aromatic compounds are almost always electrophilic substitution reactions. *(2 marks)*

3 Benzene can be converted to nitrobenzene by an electrophilic substitution reaction with a mixture of concentrated nitric and sulfuric acids.

  a What is the electrophile in this reaction? *(1 mark)*

  b Write an equation to show how this electrophile is formed in the acid mixture. *(2 marks)*

  c Write a balanced equation for the substitution reaction between this electrophile and benzene. *(2 marks)*

  d Nitrobenzene can be converted to phenylamine by reduction.

    i Write a balanced symbol equation for this reaction using [H] to represent the reducing agent. *(2 marks)*

    ii What reducing agent is actually used? *(1 mark)*

28.1 Introduction to amines

Specification reference: 3.3.11

Key term

Amines: Derivatives of ammonia, NH_3, in which one or more hydrogen atoms has been replaced by an organic group.

Revision tip

Organic groups are classified as alkyl or aryl. Alkyl groups are based on alkanes (e.g., C_2H_5, ethyl) and aryl groups are based on aromatic compounds such as benzene (e.g., C_6H_5, phenyl).

Revision tip

In amines, $1°$, $2°$, and $3°$ refer to the number of organic groups attached to the *nitrogen* atom. In alcohols, $1°$, $2°$, and $3°$ refer to the number of organic groups attached to the *carbon bonded to the OH group* (see Topic 15.1, Alcohols – introduction).

Synoptic link

Revise the factors that determine the shapes of molecules in Topic 3.6, The shapes of molecules and ions.

Revision tip

Nucleophiles use their lone pair to attack $C^{\delta+}$. Bases use their lone pair to accept a H^+ ion (a proton).

The structure of amines

Amines are classified as primary (1°), secondary (2°) or tertiary (3°) depending on how many hydrogen atoms have been replaced by organic groups.

H—N̈—H   H—N̈—H   H—N̈—R′   R″—N̈—R′
   | | | |
   H   R   R   R

ammonia   primary amine   secondary amine   tertiary amine

Naming amines

Amines are named using the suffix –amine, so:

CH_3NH_2 is methylamine and $C_2H_5NH_2$ is ethylamine;

$(CH_3)_2NH$ is dimethylamine and $(C_2H_5)_3N$ is triethylamine.

Different substituents are written in alphabetical order, so

$(C_6H_5)(CH_3)NH$ is methylphenylamine.

Physical properties of amines

Amines are pyramidal-shaped molecules with bond angles of approximately 107°. They have a lone pair of electrons which squeezes down the bond angles from the ideal 109.5° of a tetrahedron.

Reactivity of amines

The reactivity of amines is governed by the lone pair of electrons. This means that they are **nucleophiles** and **bases**.

Summary questions

1 **a** Classify

    H
    |
    N
   /   \
  ⬡   CH₃

as a primary, secondary, or tertiary amine. Explain your answer. *(2 marks)*

  b Name the amine in **a**. *(1 mark)*

2 Draw the structural formulae of the three isomers of the compound in question 1 which are primary amines. *(3 marks)*

28.2 The properties of amines as bases

Specification reference: 3.3.11

Amines as bases

Amines are basic because they have a lone pair of electrons on the nitrogen atom that can form a bond with a H^+ ion, often termed 'accepting a proton'.

$$CH_3-\overset{\cdot\cdot}{N}-H \quad H^+ \longrightarrow CH_3-\overset{H}{\underset{H}{C}}\overset{+}{-}H$$

Revision tip
The bond that is formed is called a co-ordinate bond because both the electrons in the bond come from the same atom.

Reactions of amines as bases

Amines react with acids to form ionic salts, for example:

$$C_2H_5\overset{\cdot\cdot}{N}H_2 + H^+ + Cl^- \longrightarrow C_2H_5NH_3^+ + Cl^-$$
ethylamine   ethylammonium chloride

Revision tip
Look back at Topic 21.1, Defining an acid, to revise the idea of a Brønsted–Lowry base.

The products are named in the same way as salts of ammonia, e.g., $C_6H_5NH_3Cl$ is phenylammonium chloride, CH_3NH_3Cl is methylammonium chloride.

Adding a strong base will remove the proton and re-form the amine.

$$\langle\bigcirc\rangle-NH_3^+ + Cl^- + OH^- \longrightarrow \langle\bigcirc\rangle-NH_2 + H_2O + Cl^-$$

phenylamine

The base strengths of amines

Base strengths of alkyl amines have the pattern:

Secondary amine > primary amine > ammonia > aryl amine

This is because of the **inductive effect** of alkyl groups, which release electrons, making the lone pair more available for donation. Aryl amines are weaker bases than ammonia because the lone pair of electrons is delocalised onto the aromatic ring.

Revision tip
The inductive effect is shown by an arrow along the bond in the direction of electron release.

Summary questions

1 a State the formula of dimethylammonium chloride. *(1 mark)*
   b Name and give the formula of an isomer of dimethylammonium chloride. *(1 mark)*
   c Would you expect dimethylammonium chloride to dissolve in water? Explain your answer. *(2 marks)*

2 Dimethylamine and ethylamine are isomers. **a** Give the formula of each.
   b Which is the stronger base? Explain your answer. *(4 marks)*

28.3 Amines as nucleophiles and their synthesis

Specification reference: 3.3.11

Key term

Nucleophiles: Chemical species with a lone pair of electrons with which they can form a bond with $C^{\delta+}$.

Synoptic link

The mechanism of the nucleophilic substitution reaction between ammonia and halogenoalkanes is discussed in Topic 13.2, Nucleophilic substitution in halogenoalkanes.

Synoptic link

Addition–elimination reactions of amines with acid chlorides and acid anhydrides are covered in Topic 26.5, Acylation.

Synoptic link

Nitriles can be prepared from halogenoalkanes, see Topic 13.2, Nucleophilic substitution in halogenoalkanes.

Synoptic link

The nitration of benzene is an electrophilic substitution. It is covered in Topic 27.3, Reactions of arenes.

Nucleophilic substitution reactions of amines
Reactions of ammonia and amines with halogenoalkanes

Ammonia and amines all have a lone pair on the nitrogen atom with which they can attack compounds with a $C^{\delta+}$. This makes them nucleophiles.

The reaction of ammonia with halogenoalkanes is a nucleophilic substitution reaction. It takes place in ethanol with excess ammonia under pressure.

The first step is: $RCH_2X + 2NH_3 \rightarrow RCH_2NH_2 + NH_4X$

The product is a primary amine which is also a nucleophile.

With excess halogenoalkane, further nucleophilic substitutions occur to form secondary and tertiary amines and eventually quaternary ammonium salts:

$RCH_2NH_2 + RCH_2X \rightarrow HX + (RCH_2)_2NH$ (secondary amine)

$(RCH_2)_2NH + RCH_2X \rightarrow HX + (RCH_2)_3N$ (tertiary amine)

$(RCH_2)_3N + RCH_2X \rightarrow X^- + (RCH_2)_4N^+$ (a quaternary ammonium salt)

The formation of amides

Amines will also act as nucleophiles with acid chlorides and acid anhydrides. These are usually described as **addition–elimination reactions**.

An example of the mechanism is:

Preparation of amines
Alkyl amines

Primary amines can be prepared by the reduction of nitriles, $R-C\equiv N$, with hydrogen with a nickel catalyst:

$R-C\equiv N + 2H_2 \rightarrow RCH_2NH_2$

Aromatic amines

Phenylamine and ring-substituted phenylamines can be made by first nitrating the arene and then reducing the nitro-compound that is produced with tin and hydrochloric acid. For example, with benzene:

benzene + HNO$_3$ $\xrightarrow[\text{H}_2\text{SO}_4]{\text{conc.}}$ nitrobenzene + H$_2$O

nitrobenzene + 6[H] $\xrightarrow[\text{room temp.}]{\text{Sn/HCl}}$ aniline + 2H$_2$O

Aromatic amines are used in making dyes.

➕ Go further: Explosives

Nitroglycerine is a powerful explosive that can be set off with a small shock. Unlike many explosives, it needs no oxygen from the air to allow it to explode.

CH$_2$ — ONO$_2$
|
CH — ONO$_2$
|
CH$_2$ — ONO$_2$

The products following an explosion are nitrogen, carbon dioxide, water (steam), and oxygen.

a Write a balanced equation for the explosion of nitroglycerine. (Hint, start with 4 molecules of nitroglycerine.)
ΔH for this reaction is $-29\,000$ kJ mol^{-1}, which helps to explain why the reaction is spontaneous.

b How many moles of gas are produced from the four moles of nitroglycerine?

c What factor other than the large negative value of ΔH helps to make this reaction likely to occur?

Summary questions

1 Explain why the reaction of ammonia with an excess of halogenoalkane is *not* a useful way of preparing a secondary amine. *(2 marks)*

2 What is the atom economy of the reaction of a nitrile with hydrogen? Explain. (Hint, no calculation is needed.) *(1 mark)*

3 Explain why secondary and tertiary amines cannot be produced by reduction of nitriles. *(1 mark)*

29.1 Condensation polymers

Specification reference: 3.3.12

Synoptic link

Addition polymers are covered in Topic 14.3. Make sure you understand the difference between these and condensation polymers.

Condensation polymers such as polyesters and polyamides are produced from two different monomers each with two functional groups. These functional groups react together to link the monomers and eliminate a small molecule.

Polyesters

Polyesters are made from a diol and a dicarboxylic acid.

HO—A—OH

diol

dicarboxylic acid

A and B are unreactive organic groups, for example, CH_2CH_2.

The two monomers react together as shown to eliminate molecules of water and form a long chain (see Figure 1).

▲ **Figure 1** *Making a polyester*

The links in the chain, circled, are esters – see Topic 26.4, Reactions of carboxylic acids and esters – and the chain is called a polyester, 'poly' meaning many. The groups A and B can be varied and can tailor the properties of the polymer. In Terylene, for example, A is CH_2CH_2 and B is a benzene ring.

Polyamides

Here the two monomers are a diamine and a dicarboxylic acid (or a diacid chloride).

H_2N—NH_2

A

B

These two monomers also react together to eliminate water and form a chain (see Figure 2).

▲ **Figure 2** *Making a polyamide*

The links in the chain are amides, see Topic 26.5, Acylation, and the chain is called a polyamide.

The groups A and B can be varied and can tailor the properties of the polymer. In Nylon 6,6, A is $CH_2CH_2CH_2CH_2CH_2CH_2$ and B is $CH_2CH_2CH_2CH_2$. In Kevlar, both A and B are benzene rings.

Identifying the repeat unit

The repeat unit is found by starting at any point in the polymer chain and stopping when the same group of atoms begins again.

▲ **Figure 3** *The repeat unit is in brackets*

Disposal and degradation of polymers

Condensation polymers are potentially biodegradable and can be broken down by hydrolysis – the reverse of the reaction by which they were made. This reaction is very slow under everyday conditions.

Recycling is possible, for example, fleece garments may be made from the plastics used to make soft drinks bottles.

Summary questions

1 Give the structural formulae of the two monomers for Terylene. *(2 marks)*

2 What small molecule is eliminated if a polyamide is made from a diamine and a diacid chloride? *(1 mark)*

3 Suggest two catalysts for the hydrolysis of a polyester. *(2 marks)*

1 a Explain what is meant by the terms primary, secondary, and tertiary as applied to amines. *(3 marks)*

b What feature of an amine molecule means that it can act as a base? *(1 mark)*

c Amines can also act as nucleophiles. Explain the difference between a base and a nucleophile. *(1 mark)*

2 a Name and give the shorthand structural formulae of two compounds from which propylamine, $CH_3CH_2CH_2NH_2$, may be prepared. *(4 marks)*

b For each case, outline the reaction by which propylamine can be formed, give a suitable reagent and state the type of reaction involved. *(6 marks)*

c Which of these methods is a more efficient synthesis? Explain your answer. *(2 marks)*

3 Phenylamine, , is only sparingly soluble in water and forms oily drops with a characteristic smell on the surface of a beaker of water. On adding hydrochloric acid and shaking, the oily drops and the smell disappear. On adding excess sodium hydroxide the smell and the oily droplets reappear.

a Explain why phenylamine is only sparingly soluble in water. *(1 mark)*

b Explain the observations above on adding acid and alkali. *(2 marks)*

4 Explain the difference between an addition polymer and a condensation polymer. *(4 marks)*

5 A section of a polymer molecule is shown.

a Identify the repeating unit of this polymer. *(1 mark)*

b Give the name and structural formula of the monomer from which this polymer can be made. *(2 marks)*

c What type of polymerisation is this? *(1 mark)*

d A section of a different polymer is shown.

Identify the repeating unit of this polymer. *(2 marks)*

e Identify **two** monomers from which it may be formed. *(2 marks)*

f What type of polymer is this? *(1 mark)*

g Which of the two polymers is more likely to be biodegradable? Explain your answer. *(2 marks)*

6 Both Nylon and proteins are polyamides. Explain how these polymers differ in the structures of their monomers. *(4 marks)*

30.1 Introduction to amino acids
30.2 Peptides, polypeptides, and proteins
Specification reference: 3.3.13

Introduction to amino acids

α-Amino acids (also called 2-amino acids) are the building blocks of proteins. They have the general formula,

where R can be a variety of organic groups.

Unless R is H, the molecule is chiral. They have a COOH group that is acidic and an NH_2 group that is basic. The chiral centre is marked with an asterisk.

Zwitterions

Amino acids exist as **zwitterions** in which the COOH group has lost a H^+ ion (a proton) and the NH_2 group has gained a H^+ ion (been protonated).

Zwitterions are neutral overall. But have properties similar to ionic compounds – they dissolve in water and have high melting points.

The 20 naturally occurring amino acids are given three-letter names, for example, gly for glycine (R=H), ala for alanine ($R=CH_3$), etc.

Many amino acids have functional groups as part of their R group. For example, serine (ser) has an OH group, glutamic acid (glu) and aspartic acid (asp) have COOH groups, and lysine (lys) has an NH_2 group.

Peptides, polypeptides, and proteins
The peptide link

Amino acids have two functional groups – an amine and a carboxylic acid – that can react together to form an **amide**. The resulting compound is called a **dipeptide** and this link between amino acids is called a **peptide link**, see Figure 1.

▲ **Figure 1** *Formation of a dipeptide*

Further amino acids can add on to form a chain called a **polypeptide**. Polypeptides longer than around 50 amino acids are called **proteins**.

Hydrolysis of peptides

Boiling a peptide or protein with $6\,mol\,dm^{-3}$ hydrochloric acid hydrolyses the peptide links and produces a mixture containing all the individual amino acids. The individual amino acids can be identified by **thin-layer chromatography**, see Topic 33.1, Chromatography.

The structure of proteins

Proteins have three levels of structure.

Primary structure

This is the sequence of amino acids along a protein chain and can be written using the three letter shorthand names for the amino acids, for example, gly–gly–ala–leu–asp, etc. The primary structure is held in place by the covalent bonding of the peptide linkages.

Secondary structure

Protein chains have complex shapes including helixes (spirals) and pleated sheets. These shapes are held in place by three types of bonding:

- Hydrogen bonding between, for example, C=O and NH_2 groups, see Figure 2.
- Ionic bonding between, for example, COO^- groups and NH_3^+ groups.
- Sulfur–sulfur bonds that can form between two cysteine amino acids that have S–H groups in their side chain that can link together.

▲ **Figure 2** *A protein helix held together by hydrogen bonding*

Tertiary structure

The helix or pleated sheet can itself be twisted into a three-dimensional shape held by the same types of bonds as the secondary structure. The shapes of proteins are vital for their action as enzymes, see Figure 3.

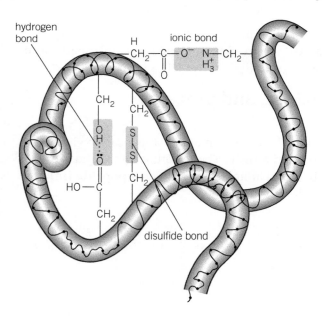

▲ **Figure 3** *Part of a tertiary structure of a helical protein*

30.3 Enzymes

Specification reference: 3.3.13

What are enzymes?

Enzymes are large protein molecules, usually globular in shape, that are found in living things. They act as extremely efficient catalysts. They are highly specific – each enzyme catalysing a particular reaction.

How do enzymes work?

Enzyme molecules typically have a cavity in their shape called the **active site**. The reacting molecules (called the **substrate**) fit precisely into this active site and are held in the right orientation to react, see Figure 1. While there, bonds are broken and new ones formed. The reaction takes place with a lower **activation energy** than without the enzyme.

Enzymes are **stereospecific**. They are sensitive to the exact shape of the substrate molecule, and so catalyse the reaction of only one of a pair of optical isomers (**stereoisomers**).

Enzyme inhibition

The shape of an enzyme can easily be altered by heating it up or by changing the pH. These factors disrupt the intermolecular interactions that hold the enzyme in its particular shape and the enzyme loses its catalytic ability – this is called **denaturing**.

Another way to inhibit the activity of an enzyme is to use a molecule of similar shape to the substrate. This fits into the active site and prevents the substrate from entering. Many drugs work like this.

Shapes of complex molecules can be modelled by computers using the principles described in Topic 3.6, The shapes of molecules and ions, and this can be used to design new drugs.

▲ **Figure 1** *The substrate of an enzyme fits its active site*

Synoptic link

Activation energy and its link to rates of reaction are discussed in Topics 5.3, Catalysts and 18.4, The Arrhenius equation.

Synoptic link

Optical isomerism is discussed in Topics 25.2, Optical isomerism and 25.3, Synthesis of optically active compounds.

Common misconception

Increasing pH makes a solution less acidic (more alkaline). *Decreasing* the pH makes a solution more acidic.

Summary questions

1   Suggest how decreasing the pH can disrupt hydrogen bonding between $C=O$ and NH_2 groups shown below.

$$\overset{\diagdown}{\diagup}C=O: {-}{-}{-}H-\overset{\overset{\displaystyle H}{|}}{N}-$$

(2 marks)

2   Suggest how increasing the pH can disrupt hydrogen bonding between COOH and NH_2 groups shown below.

$$-C\overset{\diagup O}{\diagdown}O-H{-}{-}{-}:\overset{\overset{\displaystyle H}{|}}{\underset{\underset{\displaystyle H}{|}}{N}}-$$

(2 marks)

3   List the following types of bond, which might be found in holding a substrate to an enzyme, in order of decreasing strength (i.e., strongest first).
    Dipole–dipole; hydrogen bond; ionic bond; van der Waals forces.

(2 marks)

30.4 DNA

▲ **Figure 2** *Two nucleotides react together to eliminate a molecule of water*

What is DNA?

DNA is short for deoxyribonucleic acid, the molecule that is found in all living cells and which carries the 'blueprint' for the organism. Each organism has its own particular of DNA, so there is an infinite variety of DNA molecules.

What are nucleotides?

Each molecule of DNA is a polymer made from just four different monomers, called **nucleotides**. It is the specific order of these monomers that defines each type of DNA.

Nucleotide molecules have three parts, see Figure 1.

▲ **Figure 1** *The three parts of a nucleotide molecule*

There are four different organic bases:

Polymerisation of nucleotides

Two nucleotides react together to eliminate a molecule of water, and further reaction forms a polymer chain – DNA, Figures 2 and 3.

DNA has infinite variations depending on the order of the bases, for example, CCGATTCGTA, etc.

Hydrogen bonding between nucleotides

Adenine and thymine can hydrogen bond together as can guanine and cytosine.

one nucleotide

▲ **Figure 3** *Part of a strand of DNA*

adenine
A

thymine
T

guanine
G

cytosine
C

The double helix

Strands of DNA exist in pairs, the strands being held together by hydrogen bonds. The two strands are **complementary**, where one strand has an A the other will have a T, and similarly for G and C.

Two strands wind together to form a double helix, held together by hydrogen bonds between the bases.

Genetic information is held in DNA coded by the order of the bases. When a cell divides and replicates, the double helix of its DNA unwinds. This is possible because the hydrogen bonds that hold the strands together are much weaker than covalent bonds. Then two new complementary strands of DNA are built round the originals from separate nucleotides found in the cell.

Summary questions

1 State the three component groups of a nucleotide. (*3 marks*)

2 State the complementary sequences of bases to AACCGTGTC. (*1 mark*)

3 What part of a DNA strand is responsible for its acidity? (*1 mark*)

30.5 The action of anti-cancer drugs

Specification reference: 3.3.13

Synoptic link

The shapes of transition metal complexes are discussed in Topic 23.2, Complex formation and the shape of complex ions.

Revision tip

The *cis* in cisplatin tells us that both the chloride ligands (and hence both the ammonia ligands) are on the same side of the complex. It may also be called *Z*-platin using the *E-Z* system, see Topic 14.1, Alkenes.

Synoptic link

Ligand substitution reactions are discussed in Topic 24.2, Ligand substitution reactions.

Synoptic link

Replication is described briefly in Topic 30.4, DNA.

How does cisplatin work?

Cancer cells grow and replicate much faster than normal cells.

Cisplatin is a successful treatment for a number of cancers including testicular cancer. It works by bonding to DNA and disrupting the replication of cells.

Cisplatin is square planar and has the formula

Cisplatin works by bonding to two of the bases in DNA. Nitrogen atoms on two adjacent guanine molecules, of the double helix, act as good ligands and displace the two chloride ligands. This prevents replication of the DNA.

Unfortunately this will also affect the replication of healthy cells, but as cancer cells are replicating faster, the drug has a greater effect on them.

Summary questions

1 What feature must be present on a nitrogen atom for it to act as a ligand? *(1 mark)*

2 What sort of bonds are formed between ligands and metal ions? *(1 mark)*

3 What is the oxidation state of the platinum atom in cisplatin? *(1 mark)*

1   The partially displayed formula of a tripeptide is shown below.

   a   What is meant by the term 'displayed formula'?   (*2 marks*)

   b   Circle the two peptide (amide) linkages.   (*2 marks*)

   c   The left hand amino acid in the structure is leucine, leu. Name
       the other two (from left to right) and give their three
       letter abbreviations.   (*4 marks*)

   d   The peptide is shown with both a positive and a negative charge.
       What is the name of this form of a peptide?   (*1 mark*)

   e   i   How could the tripeptide be split into its constituent amino acids?

       ii   What molecule is added to each peptide link during this process?   (*4 marks*)

   f   What technique can be used to separate mixtures of amino acids
       and identify them?   (*1 mark*)

   g   What would happen to the structure of the tripeptide in **i** a strong acid
       ii a strong base?   (*2 marks*)

2   State three types of bond that help to maintain the tertiary structure
    of a protein.   (*3 marks*)

3   How many hydrogen bonds form between the bases **a** guanine (G)
    and cytosine (C) **b** adenine (A) and thymine (T).   (*2 marks*)

4   The structure of the amino acid glycine is shown.

   a   Draw the structure of glycine in **i** a concentrated acid solution
       ii a concentrated alkaline solution.   (*2 marks*)

   b   Solid glycine has a much higher melting point than would be expected
       from its relative molecular mass. Explain this observation.   (*1 mark*)

   c   Glycine is the only α-amino acid that is not optically active. Explain
       this observation.   (*1 mark*)

   d   State the IUPAC name of glycine.   (*1 mark*)

31.1 Synthetic routes

Specification reference: 3.3.14

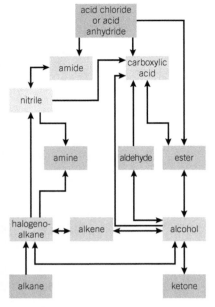

▲ **Figure 1** *Use this chart to revise organic reactions*

Synthesising molecules is about starting with one chemical and by a series of reactions ending up with another – the target molecule.

reaction scheme

Starting material ⟶ target molecule.

Revision tip

Syntheses are done in many chemical industries with the aim of making the process as environmentally clean and also efficient as possible so chemists aim to design processes that:

- do not require a solvent
- use non-hazardous starting materials
- use as few steps as possible
- have a high percentage atom economy.

Working out a scheme

Figure 1 shows how the functional groups are related. Learn the reagents and conditions for each step.

Question and model answer: How can propylamine be synthesised from ethene?

$H_2C{=}CH_2 \rightarrow CH_3CH_2CH_2NH_2$

Propylamine has one more carbon atom than ethene. This suggests that the formation of a nitrile is needed at some stage. See Topic 13.2, Nucleophilic substitution in halogenoalkanes.

Write down all the compounds that can be made from ethene and all the compounds from which the propylamine can be made.

starting material — **target**

CH_3CH_2OH ethanol

$CH_3CH_2CONH_2$ propanamide

$CH_2{=}CH_2$ ethene ⟶ CH_3CH_2X a halogenoalkane ⟶ $CH_3CH_2C{\equiv}N$ propanenitrile ⟶ $CH_3CH_2CH_2NH_2$ propylamine

CH_2XCH_2X a 1,2-dihalogenoalkane

$CH_3CH_2CH_2X$ a 1-halogenopropane

None of the compounds made in one step from the starting material can then be converted into the product, so you need more than two steps. The formation of a nitrile is required. A halogenoethane can be converted into propanenitrile so you can complete the synthesis in three steps:

Step 1: $CH_2{=}CH_2$ ethene $\xrightarrow{HCl}$ CH_3CH_2Cl chloroethane

Step 2: CH_3CH_2Cl chloroethane $\xrightarrow{KCN/dil.\ H_2SO_4}$ $CH_3CH_2C{\equiv}N$ propanenitrile

Step 3: $CH_3CH_2C{\equiv}N$ propanenitrile $\xrightarrow{Ni/H_2}$ $CH_3CH_2CH_2NH_2$ propylamine

Summary questions

1 Why do chemists design syntheses **a** with as few steps as possible **b** with high atom economies?
(*2 marks*)

2 Give a two-step scheme to convert 1-chlorobutane to butanoic acid.
(*2 marks*)

3 Give a three-step scheme to convert ethane to ethanal.
(*3 marks*)

31.2 Organic analysis

Specification reference: 3.3.6

The first step to identifying an organic compound chemically is to find out its functional groups.

Chemical reactions

⚠ Some tests are very straightforward:

- Is the compound acidic (suggests carboxylic acid)?
- Is the compound solid (suggests long carbon chain or ionic bonding), liquid (suggests medium length carbon chain or polar or hydrogen bonding), or gas (suggests short carbon chain, little or no polarity)?
- Does the compound dissolve in water (suggests polar groups) or not (suggests no polar groups)?
- Does the compound burn with a smoky flame (suggests high C : H ratio, possibly aromatic) or non-smoky flame (suggests low C : H ratio, probably non-aromatic)?

Some specific chemical tests are listed in Table 1.

▼ **Table 1** *Chemical tests for functional groups*

Functional group	Test	Result
alkene $-C=C-$	shake with bromine water	red-brown colour disappears
halogenoalkane R—X	1. add NaOH(aq) and warm 2. acidify with HNO_3 3. add $AgNO_3$(aq)	precipitate of AgX
alcohol R—OH	add acidified $K_2Cr_2O_7$	orange colour turns green with primary or secondary alcohols (also with aldehydes)
aldehyde R—CHO	warm with Fehling's solution or warm with Tollens' reagent or add acidified $K_2Cr_2O_7$	blue colour turns to red precipitate silver mirror forms orange colour turns green
carboxylic acid R—COOH	add $NaHCO_3$(aq)	bubbles observed as carbon dioxide given off

Revision tip

You will need to know *all* the organic chemistry studied in your A Level course.

Synoptic link

Look back at Topic 10.3, Reactions of halide ions, for more detail on how the silver halide precipitate, AgX, can be used to identify the halogen.

Revision tip

You cannot use this test to identify a fluoroalkane because silver(I) fluoride, AgF, is soluble in water.

Summary questions

1 A solid compound burns with a smoky flame and fizzes when a solution of sodium hydrogencarbonate is added.
   a What two functional groups does this suggest? (*2 marks*)
   b The compound's relative molecular mass is found to be 122 to the nearest whole number.
      i What technique could be used to find M_r? (*1 mark*)
      ii What is the likely formula (and name) of the compound? (*2 marks*)
   c If the M_r had been 136, suggest three isomeric compounds that it could be. (*3 marks*)
   d i Suggest another isomer of M_r 136 that does not fizz when sodium hydrogencarbonate is added. (*1 mark*)
      ii What functional group does this compound have? (*1 mark*)
   e A student suggested that the three compounds in **c** could be told apart by high resolution mass spectrometry to determine M_r to four decimal places. Explain why this would not work. (*2 marks*)

Chapter 31 Practice questions

1 The following conversions go *via* an intermediate compound. State a suitable compound in each case.

   a Ethene to ethanoic acid.

   b Ethanol to propanenitrile.

   c Propanone to 2-bromopropane.

   d Benzene to phenylamine.   *(4 marks)*

2 State the reactants and conditions for **1a** and **1d** above.   *(4 marks)*

3 How would you convert propan-1-ol to propanone (three steps)? *(3 marks)*

4 Give reagents and conditions (including catalyst if appropriate) for each of the steps in the 2-step conversion of 1-chlorobutane to butanoic acid referred to in Q1.   *(7 marks)*

5   a In the conversion of 1-chloropropane to butanoic acid, what step is used to increase the carbon chain length by one?   *(1 mark)*

   b Name the intermediate compound in this conversion and give its structural formula.   *(2 marks)*

   c The intermediate compound can also be converted to 1-butylamine.

     i What reagent and catalyst can be used to bring about this conversion?   *(2 marks)*

     ii Why is this a better method of making 1-butylamine than reacting 1-chlorobutane with ammonia?   *(2 marks)*

6 The compound $H_2C{=}CHCH_2COOH$ has two functional groups.

   a Name both functional groups.   *(2 marks)*

   b Describe a test (and its result) to confirm the presence of each functional group.   *(4 marks)*

   c Give the structural formula of the organic compound formed as a result of each test.   *(2 marks)*

32.1 Nuclear magnetic resonance (NMR) spectroscopy

Specification reference: 3.3.15

Nuclear magnetic resonance spectroscopy (NMR) is used mainly in organic chemistry to aid structure determination.

The principles of NMR

Some nuclei, such as ^1H and ^{13}C have a property called 'spin'. If they are placed in a magnetic field and subjected to a radio frequency, see Figure 1, the nuclei 'resonate'. The frequency of the resonance depends on the electron density around the atom, which shields the nucleus from the magnetic field. So the resonant frequency depends on the environment of the H or C atom.

An NMR spectrum shows the resonant frequency as a quantity called **chemical shift,** δ, expressed in units called parts per million (ppm) relative to a standard compound called tetramethylsilane, $Si(CH_4)_4$ (TMS). Using Tables of δ values, you can identify how many different types of carbon (or hydrogen) atoms there are in the molecule and what type they are.

^{13}C NMR

Only 1% of carbon atoms are carbon-13, but their resonances can be detected and therefore their chemical shifts can be measured. In ^{13}C NMR values of δ range from 0 to around 200 ppm.

^{13}C NMR spectra

Figure 2 shows the ^{13}C NMR spectrum of ethanol. It has two peaks, one for each carbon, because the carbon atoms are in different environments. The one bonded to the oxygen atom has a greater δ value, because the oxygen atom attracts electrons away from this carbon. This carbon atom is deshielded, and has a *greater* δ value than the other carbon. The other carbon, CH_3CH_2OH, is shielded by more electrons and has a *smaller* δ value. Relate the δ values of these peaks to Table C in the data sheet.

▲ **Figure 1** *Schematic diagram of an NMR spectrometer*

▲ **Figure 2** *^{13}C NMR spectrum of ethanol*

> **Revision tip**
> The heights of the peaks in ^{13}C NMR spectra are not significant, it is their δ values that are important in interpreting spectra.

Summary questions

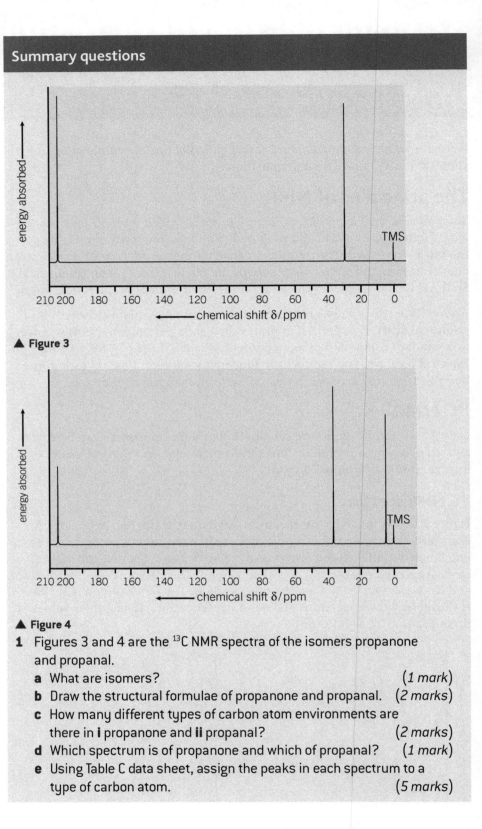

▲ **Figure 3**

▲ **Figure 4**

1 Figures 3 and 4 are the ^{13}C NMR spectra of the isomers propanone and propanal.

   a What are isomers?   (*1 mark*)

   b Draw the structural formulae of propanone and propanal.   (*2 marks*)

   c How many different types of carbon atom environments are there in **i** propanone and **ii** propanal?   (*2 marks*)

   d Which spectrum is of propanone and which of propanal?   (*1 mark*)

   e Using Table C data sheet, assign the peaks in each spectrum to a type of carbon atom.   (*5 marks*)

32.2 Proton NMR

Specification reference: 3.3.15

In proton NMR, it is the ^{1}H nucleus that is being examined. It is the hydrogen atoms attached to different functional groups that are resonating.

The ^{1}H NMR spectrum

If all the hydrogen nuclei in an organic compound are in identical environments, you get only one chemical shift value, for example, all the hydrogen atoms in methane, CH_4. But, in a molecule like methanol, CH_3OH, there are hydrogen atoms in two different environments – the three on the carbon atom, and the one on the oxygen atom. The NMR spectrum will show these two environments (see Figure 1).

▲ **Figure 1** *The NMR spectrum of methanol – the peak areas are in the ratio 1 : 3*

In ^{1}H NMR the *areas* under the peaks (shown here by the numbers next to them) are proportional to the number of hydrogen atoms of each type – in this case three and one.

The integration trace

The ratio of the peak areas is produced accurately by the NMR spectrometer with a line called **the integration trace**, shown in Figure 2. The relative areas of the peaks of this trace give the relative number of each type of hydrogen, 3 : 1 in this case.

▲ **Figure 2** *The ^{1}H NMR spectrum of methanol showing the integration trace*

The chemical shift value at which the peak representing each type of proton appears tells you about its environment – the type of functional group of which it is a part, see Table B on the data sheet.

Revision tip
^{1}H NMR spectra are run in a solution with either a solvent of tetrachloromethane or one that contains deuterium instead of hydrogen.

Revision tip
The further away a hydrogen atom is from an electronegative atom (such as oxygen) the *smaller* its chemical shift, δ.

Revision tip
The chemical shift values for proton NMR are in the data sheet in exams.

Summary questions

1   Explain why TMS gives only one line in its ^{1}H NMR spectrum. (*1 mark*)

2   **a** How many peaks would you expect to see in the ^{1}H NMR spectrum of 1,4-dimethylbenzene?
    b What would be the ratio of their peak areas?
    c Explain your answers. (*3 marks*)

1,4-dimethylbenzene

a peak split by one
adjacent hydrogen

a peak split by two
adjacent hydrogens

a peak split by three
adjacent hydrogens

▲ **Figure 1** *¹H NMR splitting patterns*

Revision tip

Spin–spin coupling is not seen when equivalent hydrogens are on adjacent carbon atoms, for example, $HOCH_2CH_2OH$ has only two single peaks in its ¹H NMR spectrum.

Spin–spin coupling

Most ¹H NMR peaks are split into particular patterns – called **spin–spin coupling** (also called spin–spin splitting). It happens because the magnetic field felt by any hydrogen atom is affected by the magnetic field of all the hydrogens on the adjacent carbon atoms. So, spin–spin splitting also gives information about the number of neighbouring hydrogen atoms, which helps you to work out structure.

The *n* + 1 rule

Figure 1 shows the spin–spin splitting patterns.

For a particular hydrogen:

* One hydrogen atom on an adjacent carbon will split the NMR signal of a particular hydrogen into two peaks each of the same height.
* Two hydrogen atoms on an adjacent carbon, will split the NMR signal into three peaks with height ratio 1 : 2 : 1.
* Three adjacent hydrogen atoms will split the NMR signal into four peaks with height ratio 1 : 3 : 3 : 1.

This is called the *n* + 1 rule:

n **hydrogens on an adjacent carbon atom will split a peak into *n* + 1 smaller peaks.**

Interpreting an ¹H NMR spectra

Each chemical environment corresponds to a chemical shift value – see Table 1 in Topic 32.2, Proton NMR.

Worked example: Analysing a ¹H spectrum

Look at the peaks in the spectrum in Figure 2.

▲ **Figure 2** *The ¹H NMR spectrum of an organic compound*

There are two types of hydrogen environments. See Table B in the data sheet. There is:

* A peak at around δ 9.7. This is the hydrogen of a –CHO group. This peak is split into four (height ratios 1 : 3 : 3 : 1) so there must be an adjacent –CH₃ group.
* The peak with δ 2.2 is caused by three hydrogens of a –CH₃ group. This peak is split into two (height ratios 1 : 1) by the one hydrogen of the adjacent –CHO group.

So this is ethanal CH_3CHO.

Summary questions

1 The ^{1}H NMR spectrum of ethanol, CH_3CH_2OH, is shown.

a What is the small peak at $\delta = 0$? What is it used for? (*2 marks*)

b Use Table B in the data sheet to state which peak belongs to which set of hydrogen atoms. (*3 marks*)

c How does the splitting of the peaks confirm your answer to **b**? (*3 marks*)

d Explain why the ^{1}H NMR spectrum of ethanol has three peaks while the ^{13}C spectrum has only two. (*2 marks*)

2 Explain why the ^{1}H NMR spectrum of methanol, Figure 1, Topic 32.2, shows no spin–spin coupling. (*1 mark*)

3

The ^{1}H NMR spectrum of methyl propanoate, is shown. Using Table B in the data sheet and the spin–spin splitting, assign the peaks in the spectrum to the appropriate groups in the compound.

(*6 marks*)

1   The ^1H NMR spectrum of ethanoic acid, CH_3COOH, is shown below.

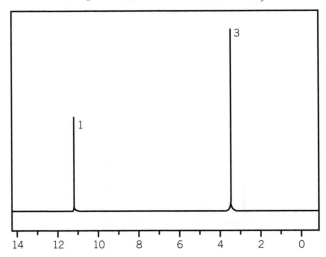

a   How many different types of hydrogen atom are present in
    a molecule of ethanoic acid?   (*1 mark*)

b   Explain why there is no spin–spin splitting of the two peaks.   (*1 mark*)

c   What peak is normally found on NMR spectra at $\delta = 0$. What
    is the purpose of this peak?   (*2 marks*)

d   Suggest a solvent for running the spectrum of ethanoic acid and
    explain your choice.   (*2 marks*)

2   a   How many peaks would you expect in the ^{13}C NMR spectrum of
        pentan-3-one? Explain your answer.   (*2 marks*)

b   How many peaks would you expect in the ^1H NMR spectrum of
    pentan-3-one? Explain your answer.   (*2 marks*)

c   Predict the ratio of peak heights in the ^1H NMR spectrum of
    pentan-3-one.   (*1 mark*)

d   Predict how the peaks in the ^1H NMR spectrum of pentan-3-one will be
    split. Explain your answer.   (*4 marks*)

e   Name the rule that predicts spin–spin splitting of ^1H NMR peaks.(*1 mark*)

3   The ^{13}C NMR spectrum of the compound buckminsterfullerene, C_{60}, is shown.

a   The spectrum has one line only. What does this confirm about the
    environment of each carbon atom in C_{60}?   (*1 mark*)

b   What compound is used in NMR spectroscopy to calibrate the zero of
    the spectrum? State its name (or abbreviation) and its formula. (*2 marks*)

c   What are the units of chemical shift used in the spectrum?   (*1 mark*)

d   How many peaks would you expect to see in the ^1H NMR spectrum of
    buckminsterfullerene? Explain your answer.   (*2 marks*)

pentan-3-one

buckminsterfullerene, C_{60}

33.1 Chromatography

Specification reference: 3.3.16

Chromatography is a family of techniques for separating and identifying the components in a mixture. Types of chromatography include:

- Thin-layer chromatography (TLC) – a plate is coated with a solid and a solvent moves up the plate.
- Column chromatography (CC) – a column is packed with a solid and a solvent moves down the column.
- Gas chromatography (GC) – a column is packed with a solid or with a solid coated by a liquid, and a gas is passed through the column.

All these techniques have in common:

- The **mobile phase** which carries the soluble components of the mixture with it. The more soluble the component in the mobile phase, the faster it moves.
- The **stationary phase** which holds back the components in the mixture that are attracted to it. The more affinity the component has for the stationary phase, the slower it moves.

So, if suitable moving and stationary phases are chosen, a mixture of similar substances can be separated completely, because every component of the mixture will move over the solid at a different rate.

Thin-layer chromatography

The mobile phase is a solvent. The stationary phase is a thin layer of silica gel (silicon dioxide, SiO_2) or alumina (aluminium oxide, Al_2O_3) on a glass, metal, or plastic sheet (see Figure 1).

Synoptic link

TLC is often used for separating and identifying mixtures of amino acids see Topic 30.2, Peptides, polypeptides, and proteins.

▲ **Figure 1** *A TLC experiment and the resulting chromatogram*

Revision tip

All R_f values must be less than 1.

When the chromatogram has run, the position of colourless spots may have to be located by shining ultraviolet light on the plate, or chemically by spraying the plate with a locating agent which reacts with the components of the mixture to give coloured compounds.

→ ninhydrin or ultraviolet light.

After the plate has been run, an R_f value is calculated of each component using:

R_f = distance moved by spot / distance moved by solvent

The R_f values can be used to help identify each component.

eluent
powdered solid
(stationary phase)
components
moving down
column
mineral wool
plug

▲ **Figure 2** *Column chromatography*

Synoptic link

The analytical use of mass
spectrometry was covered in
Topic 16.2, Mass spectrometry.

Column chromatography

The stationary phase is a powder, such as silica, aluminium oxide, or a resin, packed into a narrow tube – the column. A solvent (the eluent) is added at the top (see Figure 2). As the eluent runs down the column, the components of the mixture move at different rates and collect separately in flasks at the bottom. A mixture of amino acids can be separated into its pure components by this method.

Gas–liquid chromatography (GC)

The basic apparatus is shown in Figure 3.

▲ **Figure 3** *Gas–liquid chromatography (GC)*

The stationary phase is a powder, coated with oil and packed into (or coated onto) the inside of a long coiled capillary tube. This is placed in an oven. The mobile phase is a gas, such as nitrogen or helium which carries the mixture. This separates the components as some move along with the gas and some are retained by the oil. They are detected as they leave the column at different times – called their **retention times**. The results are presented on a graph (Figure 4) – the area under each peak is proportional to the amount of that component.

Summary questions

1   Calculate the R_f values
    of each of the spots in
    Figure 1.   (*3 marks*)

2   Why must all R_f values be
    less than 1?   (*1 mark*)

3   Why is chromatography
    usually the best method
    for separating amino
    acids?   (*1 mark*)

▲ **Figure 4** *Typical GC trace – each peak represents a different component*

GCMS — Gas chromatography–mass spectrometry

If a mass spectrometer is used as the detector, each component is fed automatically into the mass spectrometer and the compound is identified either by its fragmentation pattern or by measuring its accurate mass.

1 A thin-layer chromatogram of three separate amino acids is shown.

a i Define R_f value.

   ii Calculate the R_f value for each amino acid. (*4 marks*)

b i Using the table of R_f values below, suggest which amino acid
     (A, B, or C) is most likely to be threonine.

Amino acid	Rf value
alanine	0.21
arginine	0.21
threonine	0.34
tyrosine	0.43

   ii What must be kept the same for your conclusion to be valid? (*2 marks*)

c Amino acids are colourless. State two ways by which the spots
   can be located. (*2 marks*)

d Explain why all R_f values must be less than 1. (*1 mark*)

2 Complete the table about different types of chromatography. (*4 marks*)

	Stationary phase	Mobile phase
Thin layer		Liquid solvent
Column	Silica or alumina or resin	
GLC		

3 Describe how you would run a TLC experiment to separate a mixture
   of amino acids. (*6 marks*)

Synoptic questions

1 In the 1930s, a CFC gas, CCl_2F_2, was introduced by the American chemist Thomas Midgley as a safe replacement for refrigerant gases such as ammonia and sulfur dioxide. He inhaled a lungful of the gas and used it to blow out a candle to demonstrate that it is non-toxic and non-flammable.

   a What does CFC stand for? *(1 mark)*

   b CFCs were originally used as refrigerants. State two other uses to which CFCs have been put. *(2 marks)*

   c CFCs in the atmosphere are responsible for the breakdown of ozone in the upper atmosphere. What environmental problems does this cause? *(2 marks)*

   d In the stratosphere CFCs break down to give chlorine atoms which catalyse the following reactions:

$$Cl\bullet \,(g) + O_3(g) \rightarrow ClO\bullet \,(g) + O_2(g) \quad \text{reaction 1}$$

$$ClO\bullet \,(g) + O(g) \rightarrow O_2(g) + Cl\bullet \,(g) \quad \text{reaction 2}$$

     i What is the significance of the dot on the species $ClO\bullet$ and $Cl\bullet$? *(1 mark)*

     ii What name is given to such species? *(1 mark)*

     iii Write the overall equation resulting from reactions 1 and 2. *(2 marks)*

     iv State the function of $Cl\bullet$ in the reactions. Explain your answer. *(2 marks)*

   e The above two reactions are the **propagation** steps of a chain reaction.

     i Write an equation for a **termination** step that removes $Cl\bullet$ from the atmosphere. *(1 mark)*

     ii Suggest why this termination step is slow. *(1 mark)*

   f Reaction 1 has been found to be first order with respect to both $Cl\bullet$ and O_3.

     i Write an expression for the rate equation for this reaction. *(1 mark)*

     ii What is the overall order of this reaction? *(1 mark)*

   g Since the Montreal Protocol of 1987, CFC production has been phased out. Suggest why there is still a reservoir of CFCs in the atmosphere. *(2 marks)*

   h CF_2I_2 may be a possible replacement for CCl_2F_2. Explain why CF_2I_2 has a higher boiling point than CCl_2F_2. *(2 marks)*

   i When CF_2I_2 reacts with sodium hydroxide solution, a C–I bond is more likely to break than a C–F bond. Explain why you would expect this. *(1 mark)*

   j Describe a test for I^- ions. Explain what must be done to the reaction mixture before this test can be carried out. *(5 marks)*

2 Compound A is the halogenoalkane $CH_3CH_2CHBrCH_3$, B is the alkene $CH_3CH_2CH=CH_2$, and C is the alcohol $CH_3CH_2CHOHCH_3$.

   a State the IUPAC name of these compounds. *(3 marks)*

   b State the reactions and conditions required to convert a halogenoalkane into **i** an alkene **ii** an alcohol. State the type of reaction in each case. *(8 marks)* c   When A is converted into B, a second alkene is also formed which is an isomer of B.

   i   Give the structural formula and IUPAC name of this second alkene.   (*1 mark*)

   ii What sort of isomerism is shown by this alkene which is not shown by B?   (*1 mark*)

   iii Draw the displayed formulae of the two isomers it can form and name them.   (*4 marks*)

d   Compound A can be converted into compound D the carboxylic acid $CH_3CH_2CH(COOH)CH_3$, in two steps. Outline the two steps.   (*2 marks*)

e   i   Draw the displayed formula of $CH_3CH_2CH(COOH)CH_3$.

   ii This compound shows optical isomerism. Explain this, marking a star on the chiral carbon atom.   (*3 marks*)

3   In a petrol-driven car, a mixture of hydrocarbon fuel and air is ignited by a spark. The exhaust fumes contain the pollutant gases nitrogen monoxide, NO, nitrogen dioxide, NO_2, carbon monoxide, CO, and unburnt hydrocarbons. The amount of these pollutants can be reduced using a catalytic converter consisting of a ceramic mesh coated with the catalyst – a mixture of platinum and rhodium.

   a   What environmental problems do these gases cause?   (*3 marks*)

   b   Explain how the exhaust gases contain carbon monoxide.   (*1 mark*)

   c   Write balanced symbol equations with state symbols for the formation of **i** nitrogen monoxide and **ii** nitrogen dioxide.   (*4 marks*)

   d   Nitrogen and carbon dioxide leave the catalytic converter. Explain why they are less polluting.   (*2 marks*)

   e   What is the oxidation state of the nitrogen atom in **i** N_2 **ii** NO **iii** NO_2?   (*3 marks*)

   f   Suggest why nitrogen gas, N_2, will only react at high temperatures.   (*2 marks*)

   g   Is the catalyst in the converter a heterogeneous or homogeneous catalyst? Explain these terms   (*3 marks*)

   h   State in general terms how a catalyst speeds up a reaction.   (*1 mark*)

   i   Explain why the catalyst is coated onto a ceramic mesh.   (*1 mark*)

   j   One component of the petrol fraction is the octane 2,2,4-trimethylpentane. Draw the skeletal formula for this hydrocarbon.   (*1 mark*)

   k   In the past, petrol had the compound tetraethyl lead added to it to promote the even burning of the fuel. Explain why this is no longer used.   (*1 mark*)

   l   In cold weather, a colourless liquid can be seen dripping from the exhaust pipes of cars just after they have started. What is this liquid and how is it formed?   (*2 marks*)

4   Lithium hydroxide is used in spacecraft to remove exhaled carbon dioxide from the air by the following reaction:

   $2LiOH(s) + CO_2(g) \rightarrow Li_2CO_3(s) + H_2O (l)$

   a   Sodium hydroxide undergoes a similar reaction. Explain why lithium hydroxide is preferred in spacecraft.   (*2 marks*)

b Write the equation for sodium hydroxide absorbing carbon dioxide. *(1 mark)*

c Typically a human being exhales around 500 dm³ of carbon dioxide per day.

   i How many moles of CO_2 is this? (1 mol of any gas has an approximate volume of 24 dm³ under room conditions.) *(1 mark)*

   ii How many moles of LiOH are needed to absorb this amount of CO_2? *(1 mark)*

   iii How many grams of LiOH is this? *(1 mark)*

   iv How many grams of sodium hydroxide would be needed to absorb the same amount of carbon dioxide? *(1 mark)*

d In the laboratory, calcium oxide is often used to absorb carbon dioxide.
$$CaO\ (s) + CO_2(g) \rightarrow CaCO_3(s)$$

The table gives values of enthalpies of formation and entropies of the compounds involved.

	CaO(s)	CO_2(g)	$CaCO_3$(s)
$\Delta_f H^{\ominus}$/ kJ mol^{-1}	−635.1	−393.5	−1206.9
$S^{\ominus}$ / J K^{-1} mol^{-1}	39.7	213.6	92.9

   i Explain why CO_2(g) has the largest value of entropy. *(1 mark)*

   ii Calculate $\Delta S^{\ominus}$ for the reaction. Explain the sign of your answer. *(2 marks)*

   iii Calculate $\Delta H^{\ominus}$ for the reaction. *(1 mark)*

   iv Calculate $\Delta G^{\ominus}$ at room temperature, 298 K. *(2 marks)*

   v Is the reaction feasible at room temperature? Explain your answer. *(2 marks)*

   vi Calculate $\Delta G^{\ominus}$ at 1500 K. Is the reaction feasible at this temperature? *(3 marks)*

   vii What does the value of ΔG tell you about the reaction rate? *(1 mark)*

5 The anti-inflammatory medicine ibuprofen has the formula:

The compound is said to show **optical isomerism**. It has a **chiral centre** and is produced and sold as a **racemate**.

a Explain each of the terms in bold. *(6 marks)*

b Mark the chiral centre with a *.

c How may two optical isomers be distinguished? *(1 mark)*

d Only one isomer of ibuprofen is an active drug. Suggest why ibuprofen is sold as a racemate. *(2 marks)*

e Ibuprofen is not very soluble in water, a fact that slows down its absorption into the bloodstream. Explain why ibuprofen is not very water-soluble. *(1 mark)*

f Ibuprofen can be made more water-soluble (and therefore quicker to act) by reacting it with the α-amino acid lysine which is water-soluble.

    i What is an α-amino acid? *(2 marks)*

    ii Explain why lysine is water soluble. *(1 mark)*

    iii Why would you expect lysine to be non-toxic? *(1 mark)*

g The two form a compound 'ibuprofen express', which is absorbed more quickly. Suggest how lysine reacts with ibuprofen. (No equation is necessary.) *(1 mark)*

h The M_r values are: ibuprofen, 206; lysine, 146; compound A, the compound formed between lysine and ibuprofen, 334.

    i One tablet of ibuprofen contains 200 mg of ibuprofen. How much ibuprofen express is needed to give the same dose of ibuprofen? *(2 marks)*

    ii The M_r of compound A is 18 less than the sum of the M_rs of lysine and ibuprofen. Suggest an explanation for this. *(1 mark)*

6 4.6 g of an organic compound, A, containing carbon, hydrogen, and oxygen only were burned in excess oxygen in order to determine its formula. The products were 8.8 g carbon dioxide and 5.4 g water.

a How many moles of **i** carbon dioxide **ii** water, were formed? *(2 mark)*

b **i** How many moles of carbon were in the sample of A? *(1 mark)*

    ii How many grams of carbon is this? *(1 mark)*

c **i** How many moles of hydrogen were in the sample of A? *(1 mark)*

    ii How many grams of hydrogen is this? *(1 mark)*

d **i** What is the total mass of hydrogen and carbon in 4.6 g of A? *(1 mark)*

    ii How many grams of oxygen were in 4.6 g of A? *(1 mark)*

    iii How many moles of oxygen is this? *(1 mark)*

e What is the empirical formula of A? *(1 mark)*

f The relative molecular mass of A was found to be 46.0.

    i Name an instrumental technique for determining relative molecular mass. *(1 mark)*

    ii What is the molecular formula of A? *(1 mark)*

g The two possible structural formulae that A could have are CH_2CH_3OH and CH_3OCH_3. The infrared spectrum of A is shown:

    i What is the significance of the broad peak at $3400\,cm^{-1}$? *(2 marks)*

    ii Which of the two possible formulae is correct? *(1 mark)*

    iii What is the name of A, and to what homologous series does it belong? *(1 mark)*

  h Suggest a chemical test to confirm your answer to **g iii** and give the result you would expect. *(2 marks)*

  i Why would high resolution mass spectrometry (to four decimal places) *not* be able to distinguish between CH_2CH_3OH and CH_3OCH_3? *(2 marks)*

  j How many peaks would you expect to see in the ^1H NMR spectrum of **i** CH_2CH_3OH and **ii** CH_3OCH_3? *(2 marks)*

  k How many peaks would you expect to see in the ^{13}C NMR spectrum of **i** CH_2CH_3OH and **ii** CH_3OCH_3? *(1 mark)*

7 Kleeno is a brand of toilet cleaner sold to remove lime scale from the toilet bowl. Lime scale contains calcium carbonate, $CaCO_3$, which forms a whitish deposit. Kleeno contains hydrochloric acid which dissolves calcium carbonate.

  a Write an equation for the reaction of calcium carbonate with hydrochloric acid. *(2 marks)*

  b Kleeno claims to contain at least 10% hydrochloric acid, i.e. $10\,g$ HCl in $100\,cm^3$ of Kleeno.

    i What is the M_r of hydrochloric acid? *(1 mark)*

    ii How many moles of HCl are there in $10\,g$ of it? *(1 mark)*

    iii What is the concentration of HCl in Kleeno in $mol\,dm^{-3}$? *(1 mark)*

  c A consumer organisation decided to test the claim on the bottle that Kleeno contained 10% HCl by doing a titration. They took $25.00\,cm^3$ samples of Kleeno and titrated them with $2.5\,mol\,dm^{-3}$ sodium hydroxide solution, NaOH, using phenolphthalein as indicator. The average titre was $28.00\,cm^3$.

    i Write the equation for HCl reacting with NaOH. *(1 mark)*

    ii What colour change would take place at the end point? *(1 mark)*

    iii Why is phenolphthalein a better choice than methyl orange for this titration? *(1 mark)*

  d i How many moles of NaOH are present in $28.00\,cm^3$ of $2.5\,mol\,dm^{-3}$ solution? *(1 mark)*

    ii How many moles of HCl are present in $25\,cm^3$ of Kleeno? *(1 mark)*

    iii What is the concentration of HCl in Kleeno? *(1 mark)*

    iv Is the claim on the bottle true? *(1 mark)*

  e The Kleeno bottle warns that it should not be mixed with bleach-based toilet cleaners that contain HClO. This is because the reaction

$$HClO(aq) + HCl(aq) \rightarrow Cl_2(g) + H_2O(l)$$

    will occur.

    i State the oxidation states of each atom in the above equation. *(2 marks)*

    ii What problem is caused by this reaction? *(1 mark)*

    iii What approximate volume of chlorine would be produced by adding $50\,cm^3$ of Kleeno to excess bleach? *(2 mark)*

8 This question is about the element magnesium and its compounds. The successive ionisation energies of magnesium are given in the table.

Electron removed	Ionisation energy / kJ mol⁻¹
1st	738
2nd	1451
3rd	7733
4th	10 541
5th	13 629
6th	17 995
7th	21 704
8th	25 657
9th	31 644
10th	35 463
11th	169 996
12th	189 371

a Write an equation to represent the second ionisation energy of magnesium. *(2 marks)*

b Explain the general increase in ionisation energy as electrons are removed from the Mg atom. *(2 marks)*

c Explain how the data in the table support the electron arrangement of magnesium as 2, 8, 2. *(2 marks)*

d The mass spectrum of magnesium is shown below:

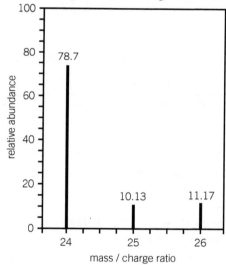

Explain what each line represents. *(2 marks)*

e Calculate the relative atomic mass of magnesium. *(2 marks)*

f State how many protons, neutrons, and electrons there are in an atom of ^{25}Mg. *(3 marks)*

g i Magnesium reacts slowly with water to form magnesium hydroxide. Write a balanced symbol equation for this reaction. *(2 marks)*

ii Give the oxidation states of each atom in this reaction on each side of the arrow. *(2 marks)*

h Describe the structure and bonding of magnesium oxide. *(2 marks)*

i Magnesium hydroxide is almost insoluble in water. Describe the trend in solubility of the hydroxides of the Group 2 metals as we descend the group. *(1 mark)*

Answers to practice questions

Chapter 17

1 a A : $K^+(g) + \frac{1}{2}F_2(g)$ B : $K^+(g) + F(g) + e^-$
   C : LE (KF) *[3]*

b $-929\,kJ\,mol^{-1}$ *[2]*

2 a $240\,000\,J$ *[1]*

b $5.55\,mol$ *[1]*

c $\Delta S = -(\Delta G - \Delta H)\,/\,T$ *[1]*

d $\Delta S = \Delta H\,/\,T$ *[1]*

e $373\,K$ *[1]*

f $+117\,J\,K^{-1}\,mol^{-1}$ *[1]*

g The sign is positive because steam is a more disordered state than liquid water. *[1]*

3 Lattice enthalpy is proportional to the square of the charge on each ion, and inversely proportional to the radius. Each ion in MgO has double the charge of those in NaF while the radii of the ions are roughly the same, because the elements are in the same period of the Periodic Table. *[4]*

4 a $\Delta S = -174.8\,J\,K^{-1}\,mol^{-1}$ *[1]*

b Negative ΔS as expected because a gas changes into a solid. *[1]*

Chapter 18

1 a i 2   **ii** 1   **iii** 3 *[3]*

Between experiments 1 and 2, [NO] is constant and $[H_2]$ doubles. The rate doubles, so Rate $\propto [H_2]^1$.

Between Experiments 4 and 5, $[H_2]$ is constant and [NO] doubles. The rate quadruples, so Rate $\propto [NO]^2$. *[1]*

b Rate = $k\,[NO]^2\,[H_2]$ *[2]*

c $8.33 \times 10^4\,dm^6\,mol^{-2}\,s^{-1}$ *[2]*

d $8.33 \times 10^{-5}\,mol\,dm^{-3}\,s^{-1}$ *[2]*

e At this time, the concentrations of both reactants are known exactly. *[1]*

2 a 1; the units of the rate constant are s^{-1}. *[2]*

b $89\,kJ\,mol^{-1}$. *[10]*

c The value is realistic. It is of the same order of magnitude as the strength of covalent bonds. *[2]*

3 D *[1]*

Chapter 19 and 20

1 a $K_p = p^2SO_3(g)_{eqm}\,/\,p^2SO_2(g)_{eqm}\,pO_2(g)_{eqm}$ Units Pa^{-1}
   (or kPa^{-1}) *[2]*

b Increase the total pressure or reduce the temperature. *[2]*

c i Increase, **ii** no change. *[2]*
NB units could equally well be expressed in kPa.

2 a i Pa;   **ii** No units;   **iii** Pa^{-2}. *[3]*

b Pa^2 *[1]*

3 a $10 \times 10^4\,Pa$ *[1]*

b 48.4 (no units) *[2]*

4 a $Pb(s)\,|\,Pb^{2+}\,(aq)\,\|\,Cu^{2+}(aq)\,|\,Cu(s)\;E^{\ominus} = +0.47\,V$ *[4]*

b Concentration of both solutions $1\,mol\,dm^{-3}$; temperature $298\,K$. *[2]*

c Pb/Pb^{2+} to Cu/Cu^{2+} *[1]*

d $Pb(s) \rightarrow Pb^{2+}(aq) + 2e^-$
   $Cu^{2+}(aq) + 2e^- \rightarrow Cu(s)$ *[2]*

e $Pb(s) + Cu^{2+}(aq) \rightarrow Pb^{2+}(aq) + Cu(s)$ *[2]*

f The solution would gradually change from blue to colourless and a deposit of brown copper would form on the lead. *[2]*

5 Bromine will oxidise Fe^{2+} to Fe^{3+}. *[1]*
$2Fe^{2+}(aq) + Br_2(aq) \rightarrow 2Fe^{3+}(aq) + 2Br^-(aq)$ *[2]*
emf = $0.30\,V$ ($Fe^{3+}\,/\,Fe^{2+}$ more negative). *[1]*

6 $[H^+(aq)] = 1\,mol\,dm^{-3}$; temperature $298\,K$; pressure of $H_2 = 100\,kPa$; electrode of platinum *[4]*

Chapter 21

1 a 0.30 *[1]*

b 0.70 *[1]*

c 2.60 *[2]*

d 11.00 *[2]*

e 4.56 *[2]*

2 a $CH_3CH_2COOH(aq) \rightleftharpoons CH_3CH_2COO^-(aq) + H^+(aq)$ *[1]*

b $K_a = \dfrac{[CH_3CH_2COO^-(aq)]_{eqm}\,[H^+(aq)]_{eqm}}{[CH_3CH_2COOH(aq)]_{eqm}}$ *[1]*

c i 2.93 *[2]*

ii 4.86 *[2]*

3 a $1.31 \times 10^{-3}\,mol\,dm^{-3}$

b $K_a = 1.7 \times 10^{-5}\,mol\,dm^{-3}\,pK_a = 4.76$ *[6]*

Chapter 22

1 a i $Na_2O(s) + H_2O(l) \rightarrow 2NaOH(aq) \rightarrow$
   $2Na^+(aq) + 2OH^-(aq)$ *[2]*

ii $SO_2(g) + H_2O(l) \rightleftharpoons H_2SO_3(aq) \rightleftharpoons H^+(aq) + HSO_3^-(aq)$ *[2]*

b The trend is for basic oxides on the left of the period to acidic oxides on the right. *[1]*

c Amphoteric means showing both acidic and basic behaviour. *[1]*

Aluminium oxide will react with both acids and bases:

$Al_2O_3(s) + 6HCl(aq) \rightarrow 2AlCl_3(aq) + 3H_2O(l)$
(basic behaviour) *[2]*

$Al_2O_3(s) + 2NaOH(aq) + 3H_2O(l) \rightarrow 2NaAl(OH)_4$ (aq) (acidic behaviour) *[2]*

2 a $P_4O_{10}(s) + 6H_2O(l) \rightarrow 4H_3PO_4(aq)$ [2]

b i More than enough magnesium oxide to react with all the phosphoric acid. [1]

$$+1 \; +5 \; -2 \qquad +2 \; -2 \qquad +2 \; +5 \; -2 \qquad +1 \; -2$$

ii $2H_3PO_4(aq) + 3MgO(s)$
$\rightarrow Mg_3(PO_4)_2(aq) + 3H_2O(l)$ [2]

iii Oxidation states above. [2]

No. There is no change in any oxidation state. [2]

c It is insoluble and will sink to the bottom of its container. It can be filtered off. [2]

d Sodium hydroxide is soluble and excess cannot be removed by filtration. So the waste water would be alkaline rather than neutral. [1]

3 a Al_2O_3 [1]

b P_4O_{10} and SO_3 [2]

c SiO_2 [1]

d SO_3 [1]

e i $Na_2O(s) + H_2O(l) \rightarrow 2NaOH(aq)$ [2]

ii $SO_3(g) + H_2O(l) \rightarrow H_2SO_4(aq)$ [2]

f $H_2SO_4(aq) + 2NaOH(aq) \rightarrow Na_2SO_4(aq) + 2H_2O(l)$ [2]

Chapter 23

1 a i $1s^2 2s^2 2p^6 3s^2 3p^6 3d^3$ [1]

ii $1s^2 2s^2 2p^6 3s^2 3p^6 3d^{10}$ [1]

b Chromium forms ions with part-filled d orbitals. Zinc ions have full d orbitals. [1]

c i [1]

ii E-Z (cis-trans) isomerism. [1]

iii The E (trans) isomer. [1]

2 a $[Cu(H_2O)_6]^{2+}$ is octahedral; $CuCl_4^{2-}$ is tetrahedral [2].

Cl^- is larger than H_2O and six Cl^- ions cannot fit around a Cu^{2+} ion [2].

$[Cu(H_2O)_6]^{2+}$ has a Cu^{2+} ion and six neutral ligands. $CuCl_4^{2-}$ has a Cu^{2+} ion and four negatively charged ligands. [2]

b Tetrahedral. Br^- is even bigger than Cl^-. [2]

3 a $[Ar]3d^9$ [1]

b There is a space in the d orbitals, so electrons can move from one orbital to another. The ligands mean that there is an energy difference between the orbitals. When an electron moves from one orbital to one with a higher energy it absorbs electromagnetic energy in the visible part of the spectrum. [4]

c i ΔE is the energy gap between orbitals, h is Planck's constant, v is the frequency of electromagnetic radiation. **ii** The frequency of electromagnetic radiation in the visible region is related to its colour. [4]

4 a The reaction starts slowly, speeds up, and then slows down again. Normally reactions start quickly and then slow down as the concentration of the reactants decreases. [2]

b Autocatalytic – a product is a catalyst for the reaction. The reaction starts as normal but as the catalyst is produced it speeds up. It then slows down as the reactants are used up. [3]

Chapter 24

1 a The green precipitate is iron(II) carbonate. The brown precipitate is iron(III) hydroxide and the bubbles of gas are carbon dioxide. [2]

b $Fe^{3+}(aq)$ is significantly more acidic than $Fe^{2+}(aq)$ and this makes the solution acidic enough to react with carbonate ions to form carbon dioxide. The Fe^{2+} solution is not acidic and the Fe^{2+} ions react with carbonate ions to form solid iron(II) carbonate. [2]

c $[Fe(H_2O)_6]^{3+}(aq) \rightarrow [Fe(H_2O)_5OH]^{2+}(aq) + H^+(aq)$
$2H^+(aq) + CO_3^{2-}(aq) \rightarrow CO_2(g) + H_2O(l)$
$[Fe(H_2O)_6]^{2+}(aq) \; CO_3^{2-}(aq) \rightarrow FeCO_3(s) + 6H_2O(l)$ [6]

2 a A chelate is a ligand with the ability to form two or more co-ordinate bonds with a metal ion. [1]

b $[Cu(H_2O)_6]^{2+} + EDTA^{4-} \rightarrow [Cu\,EDTA]^{2-} + 6H_2O$ [2]

c i 2 **ii** 7 [2]

d There is an entropy increase as the reaction proceeds from left to right because of the increased number of entities. [2]

3 a $[CuCl_4]^{2+}(aq)$ [1]

b i $CuCO_3(s)$ **ii** Sodium carbonate solution (or other solution containing CO_3^{2-} ions). [2]

c i $Cu(OH)_2$ (s) **ii** A deep blue solution. [2]

d i Aqueous ammonia. **ii** A ligand displacement reaction. [2]

e +2 [1]

Chapter 25

1 a Chiral means 'handed'. The molecule exists as two mirror image molecules that are not superimposable. [2]

b One isomer may be an active drug while the other may be inactive or even toxic. Many syntheses produce a mixture of the two isomers which will be difficult to separate. [2]

c

(structure drawing of thalidomide)

d It is a carbon atom bonded to four different groups. *[1]*

2 a propan-1-ol, $CH_3CH_2CH_2OH$ *[2]*

b propan-2-ol, $CH_3CH(OH)CH_3$ *[2]*

c propanone, CH_3COCH_3 *[2]*

3 a 3 *[1]*

b Prop- *[1]*

c Carbon number 2. *[1]*

d 2-aminopropanoic acid *[1]*

e Optical isomerism. *[1]*

f They rotate the plane of polarisation of polarised light in opposite directions. *[1]*

Chapter 26

1 a i pentanal *[1]*

ii pentan-3-one *[1]*

iii propanal *[1]*

b i and **ii** *[1]*

c i and **iii** *[2]*

d ii *[1]*

e ii *[1]*

f sodium tetrahydridoborate(III) (sodium borohydride), $NaBH_4$ *[1]*

g i and **iii** *[2]*

2 a i

(structure: H–C–C–C–C–H with H and O substituents)

ii The C=O cannot be at the end of the chain and both the carbon atoms in the body of the chain are equivalent. *[1]*

3 a i Ethanol and methanoic acid, **ii** methanol and ethanoic acid. *[4]*

b The sodium salts of the acids would be produced. *[1]*

c i $HCOOC_2H_5 + H_2O \rightleftharpoons C_2H_5OH + HCOOH$ *[2]*

ii $CH_3COOCH_3 + NaOH \rightarrow CH_3OH + CH_3COONa$ *[2]*

4 a $CH_3CHO + 2[H] \rightarrow CH_3CH_2OH$ *[1]*

b Sodium tetrahydridoborate(III) generates the H^- ion, which has a lone pair of electrons and is a nucleophile. It will attack the $C^{\delta+}$ of the $C^{\delta+}=O^{\delta-}$ but it will not attack C=C, whose double bond is an area of high electron density. *[2]*

Chapter 27

1 a i bromobenzene *[1]*

ii ethylbenzene *[1]*

iii 1,4-dimethylbenzene *[1]*

b ii and **iii** *[1]*

c *[1]*

(structure: benzene ring with two CH_3 groups)

2 The aromatic ring is attacked by electrophiles because of the high electron density of the delocalised electron system.

The reactions are substitutions because addition or elimination reactions would destroy the delocalised system and lose the extra stability of the delocalised ring system. *[2]*

3 a NO_2^+ *[1]*

b $H_2SO_4 + HNO_3 \rightarrow NO_2^+ + HSO_4^- + H_2O$ *[2]*

c *[2]*

nitrobenzene

d i $C_6H_5NO_2 + 6[H] \rightarrow C_6H_5NH_2 + 2H_2O$ *[2]*

ii Tin and hydrochloric acid. *[1]*

Chapter 28 and 29

1 a A primary amine has one organic group and two hydrogen atoms bonded to a nitrogen atom.

A secondary amine has two organic groups and one hydrogen atom bonded to a nitrogen atom.

A tertiary amine has three organic groups and no hydrogen atoms bonded to a nitrogen atom. *[3]*

b The nitrogen has a lone pair of electrons that can accept a proton. *[1]*

c A base uses its lone pair to form a bond with a proton (H^+ ion) and a nucleophile uses its lone pair to form a bond with an electron deficient carbon atom ($C^{\delta+}$). *[1]*

2 a propanenitrile, $CH_3CH_2C\equiv N$; bromopropane, $CH_3CH_2CH_2Br$ (or other halogenopropane) *[4]*

b Propylamine can be synthesised from propanenitrile and hydrogen with a catalyst such as nickel. This is a reduction reaction. *[3]*

Bromopropane may be reacted with excess ammonia to form propylamine. This is a nucleophilic substitution reaction. *[3]*

c The reduction of propanenitrile. This gives only one product whereas the synthesis from a halogenoalkane risks the formation of secondary and tertiary amines as well as the desired product. *[2]*

3 a The NH_2 group can form hydrogen bonds with water but the benzene ring cannot. *[1]*

b On adding acid, the NH_2 group accepts proton to form an ionic compound $C_6H_5NH_3^+Cl^-$, which is water soluble. Adding alkali removes the proton to restore the sparingly soluble phenylamine. *[2]*

4 Addition polymers: the monomers have a C=C bond and link together so that the empirical formula of the polymer is the same as that of the monomer. *[2]*

Condensation polymers have monomers with two functional groups which react together to eliminate a small molecule such as H_2O or HCl. *[2]*

5 a *[1]*

b Chloroethene, *[2]*

c Addition polymerisation *[1]*

d For example,

(but start at any point, and stop when the same pattern of atoms reappears). *[1]*

e *[2]*

(A diacid chloride would also be correct.)

f Condensation polymer. *[1]*

g The second one. It may be hydrolysed. *[2]*

6 Nylon has only two monomers, a diamine and a dicarboxylic acid (or diacid chloride).

Proteins are poly-amino acids. Their monomers (amino acids) each have an amine group and a carboxylic acid group. Proteins are polymerised from up to 20 different amino acids, $CH(NH_2)(R)\,COOH$, which have different R groups. *[4]*

Chapter 30

1 a A formula drawn to show every atom and every bond. *[2]*

b *[2]*

c Alanine (ala) and glycine (gly). *[4]*

d A zwitterion. *[1]*

e i Boil with $6\,mol\,dm^{-3}$ hydrochloric acid. *[3]*

ii Water *[1]*

f Thin-layer chromatography (TLC) or paper chromatography. *[1]*

g i The COO^- group would accept a proton. *[1]*

ii The NH_3^+ group would lose a proton. *[2]*

2 Hydrogen bonds; ionic bonds; sulfur–sulfur (disulfide) bonds. *[3]*

3 a 3 *[1]*

b 2 *[1]*

4 a i *[1]*

ii *[1]*

b It exists as a zwitterion in which the amine group is protonated and the carboxylic acid deprotonated, so it is essentially ionic. *[1]*

c It has no carbon atom with four different groups bonded to it. All the others do. *[1]*

d Aminoethanoic acid. *[1]*

Chapter 31

1 a ethanol *[1]*

b bromoethane (or other halogenoethane) *[1]*

c propan-2-ol *[1]*

d nitrobenzene *[1]*

2 For **a** react ethene with concentrated sulfuric acid followed by addition of water to give ethanol. Then oxidise the ethanol by refluxing with excess potassium dichromate solution acidified with concentrated sulfuric acid. *[2]*

For **d** react benzene with a mixture of concentrated nitric and sulfuric acids to give nitrobenzene. This can be reduced to phenylamine using tin and hydrochloric acid. *[2]*

3 Step 1 Dehydrate propan-1-ol to propene. Step 2 Use concentrated sulfuric acid followed by water to produce propan-2-ol. Step 3 Oxidise the propan-2-ol to propanone with acidified potassium dichromate. *[3]*

4 a 1-chlorobutane (step 1)$\rightarrow$ butan-1-ol (step 2) $\rightarrow$ butanoic acid

Step 1: Warm *[1]* with aqueous sodium (or potassium) hydroxide *[1]* with ethanol as a co-solvent. *[1]*

Step 2: Reflux *[1]* with excess *[1]* potassium dichromate solution *[1]* with concentrated sulfuric acid catalyst. *[1]*

5 a React with CN^- ions *[1]*

b Butanenitrile, $CH_3CH_2CH_2CN$ *[2]*

c i Hydrogen with a nickel catalyst *[2]*

ii Reaction with ammonia will produce some secondary and tertiary amines and quaternary ammonium salts as well as the target molecule. *[2]*

6 a alkene and carboxylic acid [2]

b Alkene – shake with bromine solution, the red-brown colour disappears [2]
Carboxylic acid – add sodium (or potassium) carbonate solution, the mixture fizzes [2]

c $CH_2BrCHBrCH_2COOH$, $CH_2=CHCH_2COONa$ [2]

Chapter 32

1 a 2 [1]

b The hydrogen atoms are not on adjacent carbon atoms. [1]

c Tetramethylsilane (TMS). This is added to the sample to calibrate the spectrum. [2]

d CCl_4 or CCl_3D or D_2O. The solvent must not contain hydrogen atoms which would swamp the signal from the hydrogens in the sample. [2]

2 a Three, because there are three different types of environment for the carbon atoms; $C=O$, CH_2, and CH_3, which differ in how far away they are from the electronegative oxygen atom. [2]

b Two, because there are just two different environments of hydrogen atoms, CH_2 and CH_3. [2]

c The CH_3 peaks and the CH_2 peaks will be in the ratio 3 : 2. [1]

d The peak corresponding to CH_2 will be split into 4 (height ratio 1 : 3 : 3 : 1) by the three adjacent hydrogens on the CH_3 group$_2$. That due to CH_3 will be split into three (height ratio 1 : 2 : 1) by the two adjacent hydrogens on the CH_2 groups. [4]

e The n+1 rule. [1]

3 a All the carbon atoms are in exactly the same enviroment. [1]

b Tetramethylsilane (TMS), $(CH_3)_4Si$ [2]

c Parts per million (ppm). [1]

d None, there are no hydrogen atoms. [2]

Chapter 33

1 a i R_f = distance moved by spot / distance moved by solvent.

ii A 0.56; B 0.36; C 0.90 [4]

b i B;

ii the solvent in which the chromatogram is run. [2]

c Shine ultraviolet light on the plate. Spray the plate with a chemical that reacts with amino acids to give a coloured product. [2]

d The spot cannot move further than the solvent. [1]

2 [4]

	Stationary phase	Mobile phase
Thin-layer	Silica or alumina	Liquid solvent
Column	Silica or alumina or resin	Liquid solvent
GLC	Oil coated on powder (or on the inside of a capillary tube)	Unreactive gas

3 Place a suitable solvent (the eluant) in a beaker to a depth of about 0.5 cm.

Mark a line about 1 cm from the bottom of a TLC plate and place a small spot of the amino acid mixture on this line.

Place the TLC plate in the solvent and place a lid on the beaker.

Allow the solvent to climb up the plate (by capillary action) until the solvent has almost reached the top of the plate.

Mark the position reached by the solvent (the solvent front).

Remove the plate from the beaker and locate the position of the spots using UV light or a suitable chemical spray. [6 marks]

Answers to summary questions

17.1/17.2

1 The first electron affinity involves the addition of an electron to the outer shell of the oxygen atom to which is being *attracted* by the positive charge of the nucleus. The second electron affinity involves the addition of an electron to a negatively charged ion which *repels* it. [2]

2 a $Mg^{2+} \rightarrow Mg^{3+} + e^-$ [1]

b The first two electrons are removed from the outer shell of the magnesium atom. The third is removed from the second shell which is closer to the nucleus. [1]

c This is the sum of the first three ionisation energies:
738 + 1451 +7733 = 9922 kJ mol^{-1} [1]

d This is the sum of the atomisation energy and the first ionisation energy of magnesium.
147.1 + 738 = 885.1 kJ mol^{-1} [2]

3 Step 0: Elements in their standard states. Step 1: $Ca(s) \rightarrow Ca(g)$. Step 2: $S(s) \rightarrow S(g)$. Step 3: $Ca(g) \rightarrow Ca^+(g) + e^-$. Step 4: $Ca^+(g) \rightarrow Ca^{2+}(g) + e^-$. Step 5: $S(g) + e^- \rightarrow S^-(g)$. Step 6: $S^-(g) + e^- \rightarrow S^{2-}(g)$ [7]

4 3013 kJ mol^{-1} [2]

5 The dip is explained by the fact that the first electron affinity of sulfur is negative and second electron affinity is positive. [2]

17.3

1 The oxygen atom, as it will have a δ− charge. [2]

2 +24 kJ mol^{-1} [2]

3 The lithium ion is smaller than the sodium ion and the water molecules can get closer the lithium ions, giving out more energy. [1]

4 $AlBr_3$ because the aluminium ion has the greatest positive charge, which will polarise the bromide ion most. [2]

17.4

Go further

a −204 kJ mol^{-1}

b Bond energies are averages over a number of molecules.

c It will tend to be stable.

d The entropy change for the reaction.

e It will be negative because two gases react to form a solid.

Summary questions

1 a $\Delta S = -284$ J K^{-1} mol^{-1} [1]

b Negative because two gases (highly disordered) form a solid (highly ordered). [1]

2 Approximately zero because all the species are solids and each will have approximately the same (low) value for its entropy. [2]

3 a −69.5 kJ mol^{-1} [1]

b It is feasible at room temperature. [1]

c Nothing. [1]

4 a $\Delta G = +14$ kJ mol^{-1} [1]

b No, because ΔG is positive. [2]

5 a +197 kJ mol^{-1}, not feasible [2]

b −208 kJ mol^{-1}, feasible [2]

18.1

1 a A product, as its concentration increases with time. [1]

b The initial rate. [1]

c Zero. [1]

2 a Use a colorimeter to measure the concentration of $CuSO_4$, which is blue. [1]

b Sample the reaction mixture at intervals and measure the concentration of ethanoic acid by titrating it with an alkali. [1]

c Collect the hydrogen gas in a syringe or inverted measuring cylinder of water. [1]

18.2

1 a i the rate constant [1]

ii 3 [1]

iii 2 [1]

iv zero [1]

v 1 [1]

b A catalyst [1]

c dm^6 mol^{-2} s^{-1} [1]

2 a i It doubles ii it trebles. [2]

b i It quadruples ii it increases ninefold. [2]

c i No change ii no change. [2]

18.3

1 This is the only point in a reaction when the concentrations of all the species involved are known *exactly*. [1]

2 a First order with respect to X, second order with respect to Y. [2]

b Rate = k [X][Y]^2 [1]

c mol^2 dm^6 s^{-1} [1]

d No, there may be other species involved that have not been tested. [2]

18.4

1 a i The height decreases ii the peak moves to the right. [2]

b The total number of molecules. [1]

c The number of molecules with sufficient energy to react. [1]

d Not at all. [1]

2 a $103\,kJ\,mol^{-1}$ *[2]*

b It is the right order of magnitude comparable with bond energies. *[1]*

18.5

1 a A and B. *[1]*   **b** C. *[1]*   **c** Step 1. *[1]*

d A catalyst. *[1]*

It is used up in step 1 and regenerated in step 2. *[1]*

e W, Y, and B. *[1]*

They appear after the rate-determining step. *[1]*

2 a $2\,NO + \cancel{N_2O_2} + H_2 + \cancel{N_2O} + 2H_2 \rightarrow \cancel{N_2O_2} + \cancel{N_2O} + H_2O + N_2 + H_2O$ *[1]*

b N_2O_2 and N_2O *[2]*

c Yes, because both NO and H_2 appear in or before the rate-determining step. *[2]*

19.1

1 CO_2 20 kPa, O_2 40 kPa, N_2 40 kPa *[3]*

2 a $K_p = p^2\,NO_2(g)_{eqm} / p\,N_2O_4(g)_{eqm}$ [1] Units Pa *[1]*

b No change. *[1]*

K_p is constant unless the temperature changes. *[1]*

c Move to left. *[1]*

Le Chatelier's principle states that the equilibrium will move so as to restore the original pressure so it will move to the side with fewer molecules. *[1]*

20.1

1 a 0.63 V *[1]*   **b** Pb positive *[1]*

c $Zn(s)|Zn^{2+}(aq) \parallel Pb^{2+}(aq)|Pb(s)$ $E^{\ominus} = +0.64\,V$ *[2]*

2 a i A phase boundary (in this case between a solid electrode and a solution). *[1]*

ii A salt bridge. *[1]*

b The most oxidised species (Al^{3+} and Pb^{2+}) should be drawn next to the salt bridge [1], the sign of the emf is that of the right hand electrode as drawn. *[1]*

20.2

1 No, electrons flow from Fe^{3+}/Fe^{2+} to $\frac{1}{2}\,Br_2/Br^-$. *[2]*

2 a A Solution of $Cu^{2+}(aq)$ ions of concentration $1\,mol\,dm^{-3}$

B Copper rod

C Voltmeter with the positive terminal connected to the copper rod

D Salt bridge

E Hydrogen gas at pressure 100 kPa

F Platinum electrode coated with finely-divided platinum

G Solution of H^+ ions of concentration $1\,mol\,dm^{-3}$ *[7]*

b 298 K *[1]*

20.3

1 A Water out *[1]*

B Hydrogen in *[1]*

C Oxygen in *[1]*

D Electrolyte – sodium hydroxide *[1]*

E Positive electrode (anode) *[1]*

F Negative electrode (cathode) *[1]*

2

Cell	Advantage	Disadvantage
Daniell		Not portable due to liquid electrolyte
Leclanché	Solid electrolyte, therefore portable	May leak if zinc case is used up
Lead–acid	Rechargeable, high voltage	Contains an acidic liquid electrolyte
Fuel cell	Water is the only product, which may be useful in space	H_2 and O_2 are gases which are difficult to store, the hydrogen may come from fossil fuels

Other suggestions are possible. *[1 mark each]*

3 There are no harmful products. The water produced can be used for drinking. *[2]*

21.1

1 Acid, H_2SO_4, base, HNO_3 *[2]*

2 a NO_3^-, **b** Cl^-, **c** OH^-, **d** SO_4^{2-} *[4]*

3 $10^{-12}\,mol\,dm^{-3}$ *[2]*

21.2

1 a 3; **b** 6; **c** 10; **d** 5.30 *[4]*

2 0.70 *[2]*

21.3

1 a i 2.44 **ii** 2.94 **iii** 2.59 *[3]*

b 4.88 *[1]*

2 a They are equal. *[1]*

b [HA(aq)] is much greater than [H^+(aq)]. *[1]*

21.4

1 a A *[1]*

b This is the alkaline region and the alkali is the same in both cases. *[1]*

c i The equivalence point. **ii** Here the acid has been just neutralised by the alkali. *[2]*

21.5

1 There is no clear end point. There would be several gradual colour changes. *[2]*

2 Strong acid–strong base and strong acid–weak base. *[2]*

21.6

1 Sulfuric acid is a strong acid. *[1]*

2 a only. *[1]*

3 4.47 *[1]*

22.1

1 0   +1−2   +2−2   0

$Mg(s) + H_2O(g) \rightarrow MgO(aq) + H_2(g)$

Note that the sum of the oxidation states is zero on both sides of the arrow. Remember there are two atoms of hydrogen in the water molecule. [4]

2 P: (+5) × 2 = +10, O: 5 × (−2) = −10. +10 − 10 = 0 [2]

3 Na: +1; O = −1 NB Peroxides are an exception to the rule that oxygen normally forms oxidation state −2. [2]

22.2

Go further

a 84.7% (Atom economy is the mass of the required product, $CaCO_3$ in this case, divided by the total mass of the reactants expressed as a percentage.)

b The limewater test for carbon dioxide. A solution of calcium hydroxide is called limewater. When carbon dioxide is bubbled into the clear solution, insoluble calcium carbonate is formed which turns the solution cloudy.

c $CaCO_3(s) + H_2O(l) + CO_2(g) \rightarrow Ca(HCO_3)_2(aq)$

Summary questions

1 $H_2PO_4^-(aq) \rightleftharpoons H^+(aq) + HPO_4^{2-}(aq)$ [2]

$HPO_4^{2-}(aq) \rightleftharpoons H^+(aq) + PO_4^{3-}(aq)$ [2]

2 +1 −2   +1 −2   +1−2 +1

$Na_2O(s) + H_2O(l) \rightarrow 2NaOH(aq)$

This is not a redox reaction as no element changes its oxidation state. [3]

3 a Burn phosphorus in a limited supply of oxygen. [1]

b $P_4O_6(s) + 6H_2O(l) \rightarrow 4H_3PO_3(aq)$ [2]

22.3

1 $SO_3(g) + 2KOH(aq) \rightarrow K_2SO_4(aq) + H_2O(l)$ [2]

2 +1−2+1   +1+5−2   +1+5−2 + 1−2

$3KOH(aq) + H_3PO_4(aq) \rightarrow K_3PO_4 + 3H_2O(l)$ [4]

3 $Na_2O(s) + H_2SO_4(aq) \rightarrow Na_2SO_4(aq) + H_2O(l)$ [2]

$MgO(s) + 2HCl(aq) \rightarrow MgCl_2(aq) + H_2O(l)$ [2]

23.1

1 They all have their *outer* electrons in 4s. [1]

2 a $1s^2 2s^2 2p^6 3s^2 3p^6 3d^2 4s^2$ [1]

b [Ar] $3d^2 4s^2$ [1]

c [Ar] $3d^2$ [1]

3 a The two 4s electrons. [1]

b It has a half full 3d shell. [1]

23.2

Go further

a Xenon is in period 5 and can use d-orbitals.

b 12

c An octahedron.

d 2

e Square planar.

f Lone pairs are closer to the nucleus than shared pairs and repel more. They take up positions as far apart as possible.

Summary questions

1 a 2 → 7 [1]

b More entities make the system more random. [1]

2 Carbon monoxide is a better ligand than oxygen and will replace oxygen carried by haemoglobin in the blood stream. [2]

3 a Br^- [1]

b Fewer Br^- ions will fit round the metal so the complex is more likely to be tetrahedral than octagonal. [2]

4 a The two Ns. [1]

b They have lone pairs of electrons. [1]

c Bidentate [1]

23.3

1 The Sc^{3+} ion has no part-filled d orbitals. [1]

2 a Green [1]

b They are absorbed by the solution. [1]

3 The change in ligand, the change in co-ordination number (change of shape) and the charge (any two). [2]

23.4

1 2:5 [1]

2 a +7 −2   +1   +3 −2

$2MnO_4^-(aq) + 16H^+(aq) + 5C_2O_4^{2-}(aq) \rightarrow$

+4 −2   +2   +1 −2

$10CO_2(g) + 2Mn^{2+}(aq) + 8H_2O(l)$ [1]

b Mn reduced, C oxidised. [1]

3 $Zn(s) + 2VO_2^+(aq) + 4H^+(aq) \rightarrow 2VO^{2+}(aq) + Zn^{2+}(aq) + 2H_2O(l)$ [1]

23.5

1 Multiply the top equation by 2 and then add the two half equations. [2]

2 It drops from 5 to 4 and then goes back to 5. [2]

3 a $S_2O_8^{2-}(aq) + 2I^-(aq) \rightarrow 2SO_4^{2-}(aq) + I_2(aq)$ [2]

b i Reducing agent; **ii** oxidising agent. [2]

c Each of the two steps involves ions of opposite charge. The uncatalysed reaction involves two ions of the same charge. [2]

24.1

1 Because the high charge density of the M^{3+} ion attracts electrons towards it, weakening the O-H bonds in the water ligands and releasing H^+ ions. [1]

2 a Bubbles of carbon dioxide gas. [1]

b The Fe^{3+} ion is sufficiently acidic to react with carbonate ions. [1]

3 The bigger the value of K_a, the more H^+ ions dissociate, but pK_a is $-\log_{10} K_a$ so the bigger K_a gives a smaller pK_a. *[2]*

24.2/24.3

1 $[Cu(H_2O)_4(OH)_2](s) + 4NH_3(aq) \rightarrow$
$[Cu(NH_3)_4(H_2O)_2]^{2+} (aq) + 2H_2O(l)^+ 2OH^-(aq)$ *[2]*

2 Fe^{3+} is sufficiently acidic to react with the carbonate ion to form carbon dioxide gas. *[1]*

3 $1s^2\ 2s^2\ 2p^6$. It has no part-filled d orbitals to absorb light. *[2]*

25.1

1 a 2-fluorobutane *[1]*

b 2-fluoro-2-methylbutane *[1]*

c 1,2-difluorobutane *[1]*

2 a *[2]*

b *[2]*

c *[2]*

25.2

1 CHFClBr. This is the only compound with four different groups attached to the same carbon atom. *[2]*

2 *[2]*

3 $H_2C(CO_2)(NH_2)$. This is the only α-amino acid that does *not* have four different groups bonded to the central carbon atom. *[2]*

25.3

1 No, the central carbon atom of the product does not have four different groups bonded to it (there are two CH_3 groups). *[2]*

2 They have exactly the same relative molecular mass and degree of polarity in their bonds so van der Waals forces and dipole–dipole forces are exactly the same. They are the same shape so they pack together in the solid state in the same way. *[2]*

3 a *[1]*

b The two isomers might have different properties as drugs – if one is the active drug, the other may be inactive or toxic. *[1]*

26.1

1 Methanal as it has the lowest relative molecular mass and therefore the weakest van der Waals forces between its molecules, dipole–dipole forces remaining the same. *[2]*

2 A hydrogen bond requires a hydrogen bonded to an electronegative atom such as oxygen. Such hydrogens exist in water molecules but not in propanone. *[2]*

3 a *[1]*

b Pentanal. *[1]*

26.2

1 It has a negative charge and a lone pair of electrons with which to form a bond with $C^{\delta+}$. *[1]*

2 The nucleophile $:H^-$ will not attack the electron-rich C=C. *[1]*

3

[3]

26.3/26.4

Go further

a $RCOONa(aq) \rightleftharpoons RCOO^-(aq) + Na^+(aq)$

b It moves to the right forming an insoluble long-chain carboxylic acid which will not wash off the paper.

c The R-group of the acid is mostly non-polar hydrocarbon which will not mix with water. The salt is ionic and, like most ionic compounds, is water-soluble.

Summary questions

1 *[1]*

2 3-bromopropanoic acid *[1]*

3 Propanoic acid and methanol *[2]*

4 a Ethanol and butanoic acid. **b** Ethanol and sodium butanoate. *[4]*

26.5

1

[2]

2 Oxygen is more electronegative than nitrogen, so water donates its lone pair of electrons less readily than ammonia. *[2]*

3 75% *[2]*

27.1

1 −240 kJ mol⁻¹ *[1]*

2 0.144 nm. (The measured value is 0.144 nm.) *[1]*

3 *[1]*

27.2/27.3

1 1,3-dichlorobenzene,

[2]

2 a $C_6H_6 + NO_2^+ \rightarrow C_6H_5NO_2 + H^+$ *[2]*

b $C_6H_5NO_2 + 3H_2 \rightarrow C_6H_5NH_2 + 2H_2O$ *[2]*

3 $RCO^+ + C_6H_6 \rightarrow C_6H_5COR + H^+$, the H^+ reacts with $AlCl_4^-$ to form $AlCl_3 + HCl$ *[2]*

4 A ketone. *[1]*

28.1

1 a Secondary. It has two organic groups bonded to the nitrogen atom. *[2]*

b Methylphenylamine. *[1]*
(Strictly, N-methylphenylamine to show that the methyl group is bonded to the nitrogen atom and is not a substituent on the benzene ring.)

2

[3]

28.2

1 a $(CH_3)_2NH_2Cl$ *[1]*

b Ethylammonium chloride, $C_2H_5NH_3Cl$ *[1]*

c Yes, because it is an ionic compound. *[2]*

2 a $(CH_3)_2NH$, $C_2H_5NH_2$. **b** Dimethylamine. It is a secondary amine and so has two inductive effects. *[4]*

28.3

Go further

a 4 CH₂—ONO₂
  |
  CH—ONO₂
  |
  CH₂—ONO₂ *[1]*

  $\rightarrow 12CO_2(g) + 6N_2(g) + 10H_2O(g) + O_2(g)$

b 29

c The production of 29 moles of gas from four moles of solid means that the reaction has a large positive entropy change, ΔS.

Summary questions

1 A mixture of primary, secondary, and tertiary amines will be formed along with a quaternary ammonium salt. These would have to be separated to produce a pure product. *[2]*

2 100%. It is an addition reaction so all the product is useful. *[1]*

3 A nitrile can have only one R group, so only primary amines can be produced. *[1]*

29.1

1 $HOCH_2CH_2OH$ and

[2]

2 HCl *[1]*

3 H^+ and OH^-. *[2]*

30.1 /30.2

1 Primary amine and carboxylic acid. *[2]*

2 It has a lone pair of electrons. *[1]*

3 a

b *[2]*

4 *[2]*

5 A hydrogen bond forms between an O, N, or F atom and a hydrogen atom bonded to an O, N, or F atom. *[2]*

6 *[2]*

30.3

1 If the oxygen atom uses its lone pair of electrons to accept a proton (H⁺ ion), the lone pair will not be able to take part in hydrogen bonding. *[2]*

2 If an OH⁻ ion removes a H⁺ ion from the COOH group, the hydrogen atom will not be available to form a hydrogen bond. *[2]*

3 Ionic bond; hydrogen bond; dipole–dipole bond; van der Waals forces. *[2]*

30.4

1 Phosphate, sugar, and base. *[3]*

2 TTGGCACAG *[1]*

3 The free OH group of the phosphate. *[1]*

30.5

1 A lone pair of electrons. *[1]*

2 Co-ordinate (dative) bonds. *[1]*

3 +2 *[1]*

31.1

1 a The more steps , the lower the overall yield.

b The higher the atom economy the less waste. *[2]*

2 1-chlorobutane → butan-1-ol → butananoic acid *[2]*

3 ethane → chloroethane → ethanol → ethanal *[3]*

31.2

1 a aromatic ring, carboxylic acid *[2]*

b i Mass spectrometry *[1]*

ii

, benzoic acid *[2]*

c 2-methylbenzoic acid, 3-methylbenzoic acid, 4-methylbenzoic acid *[3]*

d i methyl benzoate   ii ester *[2]*

e They are isomers, so they will all have exactly the same M_r. *[2]*

32.1

1 a Compounds with the same formula but different arrangement of atoms in space. *[1]*

b

propanone   propanal *[2]*

c i 2   ii 3 *[2]*

d Figure 3 is propanone and Figure 4 is propanal. *[1]*

e For propanone, δ = 200 is R**C**O (aldehyde or ketones); δ = 30 is R**C**OC
For propanal, δ = 200 is R**C**O (aldehyde or ketones); δ = 36 is R**C**OC; δ = 10 is C–**C** *[5 marks]*

32.2

1 All the hydrogen atoms are in exactly the same environment. *[1]*

2 a 2 lines *[1]*   b 3:2 *[1]*

c One line from the six hydrogens of the CH₃ groups and one from the four hydrogens on the benzene ring. *[1]*

32.3

1 a TMS. It is used to calibrate the spectrum because it appears at δ = 0. *[2]*

b δ = 4.8 OH; δ = 3.5 CH₂; δ = 1.1 CH₃. *[3]*

c The peak at δ = 4.8 is not split therefore there is no adjacent hydrogen.
The peak at δ = 3.5 is split 1 : 3 : 3 : 1 so there are three adjacent hydrogens.
The peak at δ = 1.1 is split 1 : 2 : 1, so there are two adjacent hydrogens. *[3]*

d There are three different types of hydrogen atom but only two different types of carbon. *[2]*

2 None of the hydrogen atoms has a different type of hydrogen on an adjacent atom. *[1]*

3 The peaks at δ = 3.7 and 1.2 are methyl groups as each represents 3 hydrogen atoms. The one at 3.7 is not split, so it has no hydrogen atoms on an adjacent carbon. That at δ = 1.2 is split into three (1 : 2 : 1) so it has two hydrogen atoms on an adjacent carbon.

The peak at δ = 2.4 represents two hydrogen atoms. It is split into four (1 : 3 : 3 : 1) so it has three adjacent carbon atoms, ie a CH₂ group.

Using the table we can assign the peaks as follows: *[6]*

33.1

1 Top is 0.67, middle 0.50, bottom 0.17 *[3]*

2 The spot cannot travel further than the solvent. *[1]*

3 Amino acids are too similar in properties for most other techniques to be used. *[1]*

Answers to synoptic questions

1 a Chlorofluorocarbon *[1]*

[The halogen substituents are named in alphabetical order.]

b Aerosol propellants, foam blowing, degreasing solvents, fire extinguishers. Any two of these. *[2]*

c Ozone absorbs ultraviolet radiation which can cause skin cancers, cause photochemical smogs, and damage paint and plastics. Any two of these. *[2]*

d i They have an unpaired electron. *[1]*

ii Free radicals (or just 'radicals'). *[1]*

iii $O_3 + O \rightarrow 2O_2$ *[2]*

[The overall reaction is obtained by adding reactions 1 and 2 and cancelling species that appear on both sides of the arrow.]

$Cl\bullet + O_3 \rightarrow ClO\bullet + O_2$

$ClO\bullet + O \rightarrow O_2 + Cl\bullet$

$\cancel{Cl\bullet} + O_3 + \cancel{ClO\bullet} + O \rightarrow \cancel{ClO\bullet} + O_2 + O_2 + \cancel{Cl\bullet}]$

iv It is a catalyst because it is not used up in the reaction. *[2]*

e i $Cl\bullet + Cl\bullet \rightarrow Cl_2$ *[1]*

[In a termination step, free radicals are destroyed.]

ii The concentration of Cl· in the atmosphere is very small. *[1]*

f i Rate = k [Cl•] [O_3] *[1]*

ii 2 *[1]*

[The overall order is the sum of the orders with respect to each species.]

g There was a great deal of CFCs in the atmosphere. Each Cl• can destroy many molecules of ozone before a termination step occurs. There is a large reservoir of CFCs 'locked up' in old fridges, aerosol cans, etc. which is gradually being released. It takes time for CFCs at ground level to reach the upper atmosphere. Any two of these. *[2]*

h It has a higher M_r and therefore more electrons. So the van der Waals forces between the molecules will be greater. *[2]*

i The C–I bond is weaker than C–F, i.e. the C–I bond has a lower bond enthalpy. *[1]*

j Add silver nitrate solution, and a pale yellow precipitate will form that is insoluble in concentrated ammonia solution. The reaction mixture must be neutralised by adding nitric acid to remove OH⁻ ions which would also form a precipitate with silver nitrate. *[5]*

[Neither HCl nor H_2SO_4 can be used because they would form a precipitate with silver nitrate.]

2 a A: 2-bromobutane; B; but-1-ene; C: butan-2-ol *[3]*

b i Reflux with potassium hydroxide (or sodium hydroxide) dissolved in ethanol. This is an elimination reaction. *[4]*

ii React with cold, aqueous potassium hydroxide (or sodium hydroxide). This is a (nucleophilic) substitution reaction. *[4]*

[Notice that the reagent is the same, but the conditions differ.]

c i $CH_3CH=CH_2H_3$, but-2-ene. *[2]*

ii *E-Z* (or *cis-trans*) isomerism. *[1]*

iii

, *E*-but-2-ene (or *trans*-but-2-ene)

, *Z*-but-2-ene (or *cis* but 2-ene) *[4]*

[Displayed formulae show every atom and every bond.]

d React with C≡N⁻ ions and then with HCl. *[2]*

[Adding one carbon atom always suggests the use of C≡N⁻ ions.]

e

Optical isomerism occurs when there is a carbon atom that is bonded to four different groups. *[2]*

3 a The two nitrogen oxides **[collectively called NO$_x$]** react in the air to form nitric acid which causes acid rain. They also react with unburnt hydrocarbons to form photochemical smog. Carbon monoxide is a poisonous gas. *[3]*

b This is produced by incomplete combustion of the hydrocarbon fuel. *[1]*

c i $N_2(g) + O_2(g) \rightarrow 2NO(g)$ *[2]*

ii $N_2(g) + 2O_2(g) \rightarrow 2NO_2(g)$ *[2]*

[Always check equations for balance – they should have the same number of atoms of each element on each side of the arrow.]

d Carbon dioxide is not poisonous, although it is a greenhouse gas. Nitrogen is unreactive. *[2]*

e i 0, **ii** +2, **iii** +4. *[3]*

[Remember oxygen (almost) always has an oxidation state of –2 in its compounds, and the sum of the oxidation states in a neutral compound is zero. The oxidation state of an uncombined element is always 0.]

f The N≡N triple bond is very strong and will only break at high temperatures. *[2]*

[The bond enthalpy is 945 kJ mol⁻¹ compared with 347 kJ mol⁻¹ for C–C.]

g Heterogeneous. This means that the catalyst is in a different phase from the reactants. **[Here solid catalyst, gaseous reactants.]** Homogeneous means that the catalyst is in the same phase as the reactants. *[3]*

h It lowers the activation energy of the reaction. *[1]*

i To increase its surface area. *[1]*

[In heterogeneous catalysis the reaction occurs on the catalyst surface.]

j

[Start with the displayed formula if you are unfamiliar with the skeletal form.] *[1]*

k Lead accumulates in the organs and poisons the body. It also accumulates on the catalyst and 'poisons' it. **[Either answer is acceptable.]** *[1]*

l Condensed water formed from the hydrogen of the hydrocarbon fuel combining with oxygen from the air. *[2]*

4 a A mole of lithium hydroxide is lighter than a mole of sodium hydroxide and weight is important in spacecraft. **[Both absorb the same amount of carbon dioxide.]** *[2]*

b $2NaOH(s) + CO_2(g) \rightarrow Na_2CO_3(s) + H_2O(l)$ *[1]*

c i 20.8 mol **ii** 41.6 mol **iii** 994.2 g **[The mass of 1 mole of LiOH is 23.9 g.]** **iv** 1663.9 **[The mass of 1 mole of NaOH is 40 g.]** *[4]*

d i Because it is a gas. *[1]*

   ii −160.4 J K⁻¹ mol⁻¹; negative because a gas (random) is turning into a solid (more ordered). *[2]*

[ΔS is entropy of products – entropy of reactants]

   iii −178.3 kJ mol⁻¹ *[1]*

   iv $\Delta G = \Delta H - T\Delta S = -178.3 - (298 \times -160.4 / 1000) = -130.5$ kJ mol⁻¹ *[2]*

[Remember to convert the entropy units to kJ K⁻¹ mol⁻¹ by dividing by 1000.]

   v Yes, because ΔG is negative. *[2]*

   vi $\Delta G = \Delta H - T\Delta S = -178.3 - (1500 \times -160.4 / 1000) = +62.3$ kJ mol⁻¹ ; the reaction is not feasible **[because ΔG is positive]**. *[3]*

   vii Nothing. *[1]*

[The sign of ΔG tells us that the reaction is feasible but nothing about the rate.]

5 a **Optical isomerism** – existing as a pair of non-superimposable mirror image isomers. *[2]*
Chiral centre – a carbon atom bonded to four different groups. *[2]*

Racemate – a 50 : 50 mixture of the two optical isomers. *[2]*

b

[1]

[The chiral carbon is bonded to four different groups. It may help to draw in the hydrogen atoms which are not shown on this skeletal formula.]

c They rotate the plane of polarisation of polarised light in opposite directions. *[2]*

d Racemates are difficult/expensive to separate. The other isomer is not harmful. *[2]*

e It is mostly non-polar – only the COOH group will form hydrogen bonds with water. *[1]*

f i An amino acid with the COOH and NH₂ on the same carbon atom. *[2]*

   ii It has three groups that can form hydrogen bonds with water, 2 × NH₂ and 1 × COOH. *[1]*

   iii It is present in the body. *[1]*

g One of the basic NH₂ groups could react with the acidic COOH group of ibuprofen to form a salt. *[1]*

h i 200 × 334 / 206 = 324.3 mg *[2]*

   ii A molecule of water (M_r 18) is eliminated in the reaction. *[1]*

[The two form a salt with water as a by-product.]

6 a i 0.2 mol CO_2 **ii** 0.3 mol H_2O *[2]*

[To find the number of moles, divide the mass in grams by A_r.]

b i 0.2 mol C *[1]*   **ii** 2.4 g C *[1]*

c 0.6 mol (ii) 0.6 g *[2]*

d i 3.0 g *[1]* **ii** 1.6 g *[1]* **iii** 0.1 mol *[1]*

e C_2H_6O *[1]*

f i Mass spectrometry *[1]*

   ii C_2H_6O *[1]*

[M_r of the empirical formula is 46, so the empirical and molecular formulae are the same.]

g i This is an O–H stretch so A has an O–H group *[2]*

   ii It must be CH_3CH_2OH. *[1]*

   iii ethanol, alcohols *[1]*

h Warm with yellow acidified potassium dichromate solution. The solution would turn to green. *[2]*

i They are isomers and would therefore give exactly the same result. *[2]*

j i 3;   **ii** 1 *[2]*

[All the hydrogen atoms in CH_3OCH_3 are in identical environments.]

k i 2   **ii** 1 *[1]*

[Both carbon atoms in CH_3OCH_3 are in identical environments.]

7 a $CaCO_3(s) + 2HCl(aq) \rightarrow CaCl_2(aq) + H_2O(l) + CO_2(g)$ *[2]*

b i 36.5 *[1]* **ii** 0.27 mol *[1]* **iii** 2.7 mol dm^{-3} *[1]*

c i $HCl(aq) + NaOH(aq) \rightarrow NaCl(aq) + H_2O(l)$ *[1]*

  ii Colourless to pink. *[1]*

  iii The colour change is more distinct than red to yellow. *[1]*

d i 0.07 mol *[1]*

[Use the equation No. of moles = c × V / 1000.]

  ii 0.07 mol *[1]*

  iii 2.8 mol dm^{-3} *[1]*

  iv Yes *[1]*

e i +1+1−2 +1−1   0   +1−2
  $HClO(aq) + HCl(aq) \rightarrow Cl_2(g) + H_2O(l)$ *[2]*

  ii Chlorine is a toxic gas. *[1]*

  iii 50 cm^3 Kleeno contains 50 × 2.8 / 1000 mol = 0.14 mol. This produces 0.14 × 24 dm^3 of gas at room conditions. 3.4 dm^3 chlorine. **['Excess' means that there is enough bleach to react with all the Kleeno.]** *[2]*

8 a $Mg^+(g) \rightarrow Mg^{2+}(g) + e^-$ *[2]*

[The state symbols are essential. This is *not* Mg(g) → Mg^{2+}(g) +2e$^-$]

b As each successive electron is removed, it comes from a more highly positively charged ion. *[2]*

c There is a large jump in IE after two electrons have been lost and another jump after a further eight electrons have been lost. *[2]*

d Magnesium has three isotopes of mass numbers 24, 25, and 26. *[2]*

e $\dfrac{(24 \times 78.7) + (25 \times 10.13) + (26 \times 11.17)}{100} = 24.32$ *[2]*

f 12 protons, 13 neutrons, 12 electrons. *[3]*

g i $Mg(s) + 2H_2O(l) \rightarrow Mg(OH)_2(s) + H_2(g)$ *[2]*
   0   +1−2   +2 −2+1   0

  ii $Mg(s) + 2H_2O(l) \rightarrow Mg(OH)_2(s) + H_2(g)$ *[2]*

[Remember the oxidation state of an uncombined element is always 0. The sum of the oxidation states in a neutral compound is zero.]

h Giant ionic. *[2]*

i The solubility increases. *[1]*

Periodic Table

The Periodic Table of the elements

Key

relative atomic mass
atomic symbol
name
atomic (proton) number

Example:
1.0 **H** hydrogen 1

(1)	(2)											(13)	(14)	(15)	(16)	(17)	0
																	4.0 **He** helium 2
6.9 **Li** lithium 3	9.0 **Be** beryllium 4											10.8 **B** boron 5	12.0 **C** carbon 6	14.0 **N** nitrogen 7	16.0 **O** oxygen 8	19.0 **F** fluorine 9	20.2 **Ne** neon 10
23.0 **Na** sodium 11	24.3 **Mg** magnesium 12	(3)	(4)	(5)	(6)	(7)	(8)	(9)	(10)	(11)	(12)	27.0 **Al** aluminium 13	28.1 **Si** silicon 14	31.0 **P** phosphorus 15	32.1 **S** sulfur 16	35.5 **Cl** chlorine 17	39.9 **Ar** argon 18
39.1 **K** potassium 19	40.1 **Ca** calcium 20	45.0 **Sc** scandium 21	47.9 **Ti** titanium 22	50.9 **V** vanadium 23	52.0 **Cr** chromium 24	54.9 **Mn** manganese 25	55.8 **Fe** iron 26	58.9 **Co** cobalt 27	58.7 **Ni** nickel 28	63.5 **Cu** copper 29	65.4 **Zn** zinc 30	69.7 **Ga** gallium 31	72.6 **Ge** germanium 32	74.9 **As** arsenic 33	79.0 **Se** selenium 34	79.9 **Br** bromine 35	83.8 **Kr** krypton 36
85.5 **Rb** rubidium 37	87.6 **Sr** strontium 38	88.9 **Y** yttrium 39	91.2 **Zr** zirconium 40	92.9 **Nb** niobium 41	95.9 **Mo** molybdenum 42	[98] **Tc** technetium 43	101.1 **Ru** ruthenium 44	102.9 **Rh** rhodium 45	106.4 **Pd** palladium 46	107.9 **Ag** silver 47	112.4 **Cd** cadmium 48	114.8 **In** indium 49	118.7 **Sn** tin 50	121.8 **Sb** antimony 51	127.6 **Te** tellurium 52	126.9 **I** iodine 53	131.3 **Xe** xenon 54
132.9 **Cs** caesium 55	137.3 **Ba** barium 56	138.9 **La*** lanthanum 57	178.5 **Hf** hafnium 72	180.9 **Ta** tantalum 73	183.8 **W** tungsten 74	186.2 **Re** rhenium 75	190.2 **Os** osmium 76	192.2 **Ir** iridium 77	195.1 **Pt** platinum 78	197.0 **Au** gold 79	200.6 **Hg** mercury 80	204.4 **Tl** thallium 81	207.2 **Pb** lead 82	209.0 **Bi** bismuth 83	[209] **Po** polonium 84	[210] **At** astatine 85	[222] **Rn** radon 86
[223] **Fr** francium 87	[226] **Ra** radium 88	[227] **Ac†** actinium 89	[261] **Rf** rutherfordium 104	[262] **Db** dubnium 105	[266] **Sg** seaborgium 106	[264] **Bh** bohrium 107	[277] **Hs** hassium 108	[268] **Mt** meitnerium 109	[271] **Ds** darmstadtium 110	[272] **Rg** roentgenium 111							

Elements with atomic numbers 112-116 have been reported but not fully authenticated

* 58 – 71 Lanthanides

140.1 **Ce** cerium 58	140.9 **Pr** praseodymium 59	144.2 **Nd** neodymium 60	144.9 **Pm** promethium 61	150.4 **Sm** samarium 62	152.0 **Eu** europium 63	157.3 **Gd** gadolinium 64	158.9 **Tb** terbium 65	162.5 **Dy** dysprosium 66	164.9 **Ho** holmium 67	167.3 **Er** erbium 68	168.9 **Tm** thulium 69	173.0 **Yb** ytterbium 70	175.0 **Lu** lutetium 71

† 90 – 103 Actinides

232.0 **Th** thorium 90	231.0 **Pa** protactinium 91	238.0 **U** uranium 92	237.0 **Np** neptunium 93	239.1 **Pu** plutonium 94	243.1 **Am** americium 95	247.0 **Cm** curium 96	247.1 **Bk** berkelium 97	252.1 **Cf** californium 98	[252] **Es** einsteinium 99	[257] **Fm** fermium 100	[258] **Md** mendelevium 101	[259] **No** nobelium 102	[260] **Lr** lawrencium 103

Data

Table A Infrared

Bond	Wavenumber / cm^{-1}
C—H	2850–3300
C—C	750–1100
C=C	1620–1680
C=O	1680–1750
C—O	1000–1300
O—H (alcohols)	3230–3550
O—H (acids)	2500–3000
N—H	3300–3500

Table B ^{1}H NMR chemical shift data

Type of proton	δ/ppm
ROH	0.5–5.0
RCH$_3$	0.7–1.2
RNH$_2$	1.0–4.5
R$_2$CH$_2$	1.2–1.4
R$_3$CH	1.4–1.6
R—C(=O)—C—H	2.1–2.6
R—O—C—H	3.1–3.9
RCH$_2$Cl or Br	3.1–4.2
R—C(=O)—O—C—H	3.7–4.1
R₂C=CH (C=C)	4.5–6.0
R—C(=O)—H	9.0–10.0
R—C(=O)—O—H	10.0–12.0

Table C ^{13}C NMR chemical shift data

Type of carbon	δ/ppm
—C—C—	5–40
R—C—Cl or Br	10–70
R—C(=O)—C—	20–50
R—C—N	25–60
—C—O— alcohols, ethers or esters	50–90
C=C	90–150
R—C≡N	110–125
(benzene ring)	110–160
R—C(=O)— esters or acids	160–185
R—C(=O)— aldehydes or ketones	190–220

Phosphate and sugars

phosphate

glucose

2-deoxyribose

Bases

adenine

guanine

cytosine

thymine

Amino acids

alanine

aspartic acid

cysteine

lysine

phenylalanine

serine

Haem B